THE NEW PRIESTHOOD

OTHER BOOKS BY RALPH E. LAPP

THE
NEW
PRIESTHOOD

THE SCIENTIFIC ELITE
AND THE USES OF POWER

by Ralph E. Lapp

HARPER & ROW, PUBLISHERS
New York, Evanston, London

FIRST EDITION

LIBRARY OF CONGRESS CATALOG CARD NUMBER: 65-14686

C-P

To Leo Szilard
a prodigious innovator in the ways
of science and society

CONTENTS

THE NEW PRIESTHOOD

THE
NEW
1 PRIESTHOOD

When he was campaigning in 1912 Woodrow Wilson spoke out: "What I fear is a government of experts. God forbid that in a democratic society we should resign the task and give the government over to experts. What are we for if we are to be scientifically taken care of by a small number of gentlemen who are the only men who understand the job? Because if we don't understand the job, then we are not a free people."

Ever since Einstein sent his historic letter to Roosevelt leading to the creation of the A-bomb the world of science has been in spasmodic and not always successful communication with society. The dialogues of scientist-to-government and scientist-to-people have been beset with formidable and growing obstacles. The increasing specialization and complexity of science has broken off the conversation links between the layman and the laboratory. Yet the fruits of science, unlike the grapes which Tantalus could not reach, hang heavy on the vine and are within reach. Civilization wants the material benefits of modern science and its companion technology, and it is most unlikely that any modern society such as ours will turn its back on science.

Our democratic society needs to ask: What are the goals of science and how are they conjugated with those of our nation? The goals of science focus upon the exploration of the unknown and

the enlargement of knowledge. Very often the greatest discoveries
come when a man sees relationships between things which no one
recognized before—or sees these in a new light. But usually science
expands into the unknown like a huge amoeba, moving first this
way and then that, seeking the virgin and the fertile. Its goals are
determined by opportunity and chance, and sometimes design. The
lone researcher of prewar days followed his scientific nose or
hunch, or plodded along a path followed by others. Today, more
often than not, the lone investigator is a *rara avis;* most scientists
team up to work together toward agreed upon objectives. These
may be small groups of two or three, or much larger communities
of a score of researchers. A single experiment may involve a hundred scientists, technicians, and engineers; it may cost hundreds
of thousands of dollars. When such numbers of men and such
amounts of money are involved, the research is no longer unspeci-
fied as to objective, and very often it is financed by the federal
government. Here science and society intersect; the latter fosters
the former because it believes in the inherent goodness of the work
or because the work may actually define a security or prestige or
some other benefit. The over-all goal of science is clear to its practitioners: more knowledge. This is sufficient to egg on the researcher, who rarely pauses to inquire how his work may relate to
social benefits.

It is the thesis of this book that democracy faces its most severe
test in preserving its traditions in an age of scientific revolution. To
be sure, there is no danger of a coup or take-over, for there is no
conspiracy of scientists about to seize the reins of government.
These quiet "usurpers" are strange characters indeed, for while
they hold the key to prodigious power they show no signs of aspiring to political power. But whether they aspire or not, scientists in
key advisory positions wield enormous power. The ordinary checks
and balances of a democracy fail when the Congress, for example,
is incapable of intelligent discourse on vital issues.

The danger to our democracy is that national policy will be
decided by the few acting without even attempting to enter into a
public discourse on the issues. If these few are the best technically

qualified then, according to an updating of Plato's original definition, our democracy will become a timocracy.

The number of science literates in the United States is growing,
but even so it represents at most only a few per cent of the population. The sinews of our democracy will be strained as the nation
becomes more and more dependent for its welfare upon the even
fewer people who form a scientific and technical elite. When the
fortunes of so many depend in the ultimate upon so few how can
controls be fashioned prudently and policy formulated wisely? It
is worth recalling that while Einstein acted most democratically in
appealing as a citizen to the highest authority in the land, thereafter the process by which his proposal was handled was scarcely in
the tradition of democracy. Atomic energy development became a
highly secret undertaking, so secret in fact, that only a handful of
Congressmen approved the funds for the bomb work. This action
was taken in the name of security, but it became a pattern for much
research and development in the postwar period. Even if no formal
secrecy is invoked by the government an issue might as well be
classified "secret" if the people in a democracy are incapable of
carrying on an intelligent discussion of it. Here both scientists and
laymen bear a pressing responsibility to establish a dialogue and to
maintain it. If this is not done we face the real danger of a layered
society in which a scientist elite fraction floats on top and dominates
our policy-making. The danger is that a new priesthood of scientists
may usurp the traditional roles of democratic decision-making.

At the turn of the century our nation's economy was geared to
the horse and buggy and to the animal-drawn plow. Man's educational requirements were minimal; a strong back and good health
were of prime importance. For every dozen people graduating from
grade school, three would earn a high school certificate and only
one would win a college degree. Scientists and engineers were a
rarity; in a total of five hundred grade school graduates only one
student might emerge with a degree in science. And those honored
with a Ph.D. in science were so few that all of them in the United
States could gather in a college auditorium without crowding.

The triple impact of the internal combustion engine, electronics, and mass production shifted the nation's economic center of gravity from the farm to the factory. Simultaneously the locus of man's strength moved upward from his backbone toward his brain, although the production line still put more emphasis on nimble hands than on intellect. Few jobs existed in the labor force which could not be filled by a few hours of training a normally intelligent person. When the Great Depression pressed down upon the industrial growth of America over half the labor force were grade school graduates, and one quarter could boast of a high school diploma; college graduates constituted only about 3 per cent of the labor force and there was only one scientist-engineer graduate for every 250 workers. The Ph.D. scientist was a distinctly academic creature; only a few strayed from the college campus to work at practical things in industry. Of course, during the deadliest days of the Depression, the highly educated sometimes concealed their academic attainments, for they were of little value. Nonetheless, the requirements of the nation were beginning to place a premium upon the educated worker.

World War II accelerated the trend for more and more education, and the postwar years suddenly enshrined the scientist as the great innovator in society. Almost overnight the atomic scientists emerged from the solitude of their laboratories and invaded the marketplace of man. Their quiet sanctum of ideas exploded into the real world with shattering impact, which reverberated like shock waves in an echo chamber. Science had become a revolutionary new force in the world and the demand for scientists spiraled. Big business and government enticed Ph.D.s from the campus. Research and development (R & D) skyrocketed to the proportions of a major industry. Congress appropriated over $15 billion for R & D activities in the early sixties and industry financed about a third as much for its own programs. The highest priority was now assigned to the highest part of man's anatomy—the three-pound computer so wondrously fashioned that it had no electronic substitute except for purely digital operations where speed and not thought was of paramount concern.

With the development of high-speed computers and information-handling devices that permit storage and retrieval of vast amounts of data, great advances have been made possible not only in mass production of objects but also in the control of industrial processes. An M.I.T. professor, the late Norbert Wiener, coined the word "cybernetics," borrowing from the Greek word for "steersman" to apply to the control of processes and machines (and man as well) by the acquisition and "feedback" to the system of pertinent information about its functioning and objective. A very elementary cybernated system is a thermostatic control used in millions of American households for turning on and off heat or cooling in response to a thermometer that measures the ambient temperature of the air. However, the data-handling capacity of a computer allows it to store in its magnetic memory an incredible inventory of facts so that applications can be made to very complex situations. Furthermore, the computer serves as more than a repository for facts; one can program into it instructions on how to respond (make decisions) to situations and even how to adapt to new situations on the basis of elementary learning. It is this capability that sends a chill down the spine of a layman; for he senses that man's three-pound computer will be no match for modern competition.

Actually, the computer has assumed command and control of certain industrial and business operations; it may even usurp managerial functions. Complex petrochemical plants have been fully cybernated with hundreds of instruments delicately sensing the chemical pulse of the process, communicating their findings to a central computer and then receiving back commands which alter the operation if it deviates one iota from optimal conditions. No men could hope to match the speedy and flawless caretaking of the twenty-four-hour-a-day electronic mastermind. *The priests have within their temple a wondrous array of "magical" apparatus.*

The precision, speed, and information capacity of the computer qualify it to displace man in many routine jobs. The blue-collar worker was the first to feel this displacement, but now white-collar workers are finding that their services can be equaled or surpassed by machines. For example, a postal worker sorts mail using me-

chanical aids, but he still uses his eyes to read the address before
he punches the proper key to dispatch a letter to its appropriate
bin. Even the sorter's eye is now dispensable. A number of American companies have developed electro-optical "readers" which are
semi-intelligent in that they have been "taught" to recognize
numerical and alphabetical characters. One machine now in experimental operation automatically casts its "eye" over envelopes
and converts the black-and-white recognition pattern into electronic pulses which identify individual letters of the alphabet.
Logic systems within the machine then synthesize the information
and determine which state of the union is involved. Letters flow
through the machine at the rate of 27,000 per hour and flip into
fifty separate bins at the other end, ready to be carted off to appropriate mail trains or planes. The ability to read would seem to be a
human characteristic—what an irony that man develops a device
that reads while 700 million of his fellow men are adult illiterates!

We are still in the infancy of the cybernetics age, which is not
much more than a decade old in its computer phase. It is still in its
"dumb" stage, yet over $6 billion worth of computers are in use
today, and by 1970 a conservative estimate projects a $22 billion
inventory of computers throughout the world. This mushroom
growth of computers is spectacular, but it tends to conceal an underlying change in the nature of the product. The natural evolution of
computers proceeds from the dumb stage to machines that will
effectively take the THINK sign off the IBM office wall and
incorporate it in their innards.

Machines that think, even if they are relatively dim-witted, can
bump white-collar workers off the payroll. Blue-collar workers have
already felt the bumping effect and now it is the white-collar employees who will feel the impact. Naturally the first to be displaced
(or in the case of teen-agers, never *placed*) will be the under-
educated. How will these misfits regard their role in a society which
is keyed to high I.Q.s while they are condemned to intellectual
serfdom?

It goes without saying that research and development will be a major industry in the United States and that the prosecution of research programs will require the training of scientists and engineers to the doctorate level; some 20,000 Ph.D.s will be needed each year. This used to be the number of soldiers in a full army division. The total corps of scientists or engineers with professional qualifications, meaning a degree from college, will swell to roughly 4.5 million by 1980. This means that there will be one scientist or engineer for every twenty-two people in the United States labor force.

In 1980 the high school graduate who does not go to college cannot aspire to much of a position in the technological world. Since there will be relatively little requirement for farmers or ditch diggers, the "uneducated" high school graduate will be shunted into the great pool of service workers or into the semiskilled category of technicians, repairmen, and so forth; his probable lifetime earnings will be very much related to his educational rank. Many, through no fault of their own except that they were born with a low I.Q., will occupy the lower social levels in this new society. Others, with adequate mental equipment but lacking incentive or opportunity, will reach maturity only to be frustrated by the kind of jobs available to them. There will, of course, be openings for plumbers and bricklayers, but repairmen will find that they need more training to service the kind of products that industry will produce in 1980. And unless quality control is better than it has been in recent years, there will be an increasing number of service calls. This structuring of the labor force cannot help but make a vast multitude of Americans feel that they are "left out" of full participation in society. Their basic wants may be fulfilled, as were those of the great slave populations when Greek culture was in full flower, but they will tend to feel unfulfilled as citizens. They may never grow to revolt against the computer or its designers and caretakers, but surely resentment will smolder in their breasts as they contemplate their lot.

This gloomy forecast of the average man's utility in the near future poses a great dilemma for a democratic society in which national planning is not always esteemed by the voters. Happily, the

U.S. Senate Committee on Labor and Public Welfare under the guidance of Joseph Clark of Pennsylvania thoroughly investigated the effect of automation and technology on employment and manpower, and in August, 1964, a National Commission on Technology, Automation, and Economic Progress was established. Essentially a fact-finding body, the new Commission will serve to focus national attention on adjusting our nation's manpower to the demands and effects of the computer era. It is none too soon for the nation to assess the impact of technology upon our future society. The computer made its debut early in the 1950s, and by 1963 the United States alone had a total of $4.1 billion invested in these electronic wizards. A $15 billion value has been projected for the total of all such devices in the United States by 1970 and it is estimated that there will be two million people then employed in data processing. This fast-moving technology will strain to the limit the ability of a great nation to react effectively so that people are not "bumped down" from the present jobs and forced to seek employment elsewhere if, as the New York *Times* wryly commented, "they do not have the good grace to disappear when they are no longer needed."

Thomas J. Watson, chairman of the board of IBM, noted: "Most of the unemployed people we see today are victims of this bumping-down process. They are the uneducated, the unskilled, the older workers, and teen-agers. . . . These young people are vulnerable because of inexperience, because they lack seniority and, overshadowing everything else, because they have not acquired either the educational background or the skills needed in today's labor market." One might go one step further and conclude that if these young people, a new voting bloc in America, are not well qualified for employment, how can they really be fully capable of participating in our democratic form of government? Thomas Jefferson wrote: "To furnish the citizens with full and correct information is a matter of the highest importance. If we think them not enlightened enough to exercise their control with a wholesome discretion, the remedy is not to take it from them but to inform their discretion by education." Jefferson's prescription, given so long ago, is still valid today, but it is much harder to follow.

Alfred North Whitehead's words of almost half a century ago have dramatic currency: "In the conditions of modern life the rule is absolute: the race which does not value trained intelligence is doomed. Not all your heroism, not all your victories on land or at sea, can move back the finger of fate. Today we maintain ourselves. Tomorrow science will have moved forward yet one more step, and there will be no appeal from the judgment which will then be pronounced upon the uneducated."

Whitehead's judgment could be grim indeed if interpreted purely in terms of masses of unemployed. But even if our economy manages to achieve full employment, the condition will be that envisioned by Dr. L. R. Hafstad, director of research for General Motors. He foresees "a larger and larger population . . . supported on and by the work of a smaller and smaller fraction of highly trained creative specialists lead[ing] to a social structure like that of an inverted pyramid."

As even a school child knows, an inverted pyramid represents a most unstable geometrical form. A society that depends upon a few, whether they be the rich or the brainy or the blooded, is not the most inclined to be a stable democracy. This disinclination is aggravated in the case where the dominant feature of a modern society is its dependence upon science and technology. Inevitably the policy decisions of such a society become deeply snarled in the vocabulary and substance of technology. The technically qualified rarely include politicians or administrators of sprawling bureaucracies. Thus, by default, the scientists and technical experts tend to invade the decision-making circles and their influence grows with the expansion of technology in our economy.

The yawning gap between scientist and layman is more than just a casual difference of vocabulary. The world of the scientist is so remote, so invisible to the untutored, that it is as though scientist and layman are of different species. Few scientists are accomplished in the area of public discourse. Though they speak out they are not apt to be understood and those bystanders who translate for them do only a partial job of exposition. Furthermore, the pace of modern science is one of constant acceleration so that many despair of effective communication.

A backward glance at life in our country shows how dramatically technology has altered man's ways both at work and at home. In my own family, my mother's father worked all his life as a blacksmith, earning his living by sheer muscle-power; he never got beyond eighth grade in school. My father graduated from high school and worked most of his life as a machinist in an automobile plant but then switched to a new livelihood late in life working with IBM machines in an aircraft company. I went to school seven more years than my father and began my professional career working on the A-bomb project. The horse, the auto and plane, then the atom mark the occupational highlights in one man's family during this century. (Where we go from here is uncertain, but my older boy aspires to be a lifeguard.)

The escalating educational attainments cited in this personal retrospection need to be viewed on a national scale. Today, one in every two people in the labor force has a high school diploma, one in sixty-six has a college degree in science or engineering and one in every seven hundred has a doctorate in science or engineering.

Brainpower is now considered such a valuable asset that the government heavily subsidizes the education of scientists and engineers. Our nation's colleges and universities are now turning out over 8,000 Ph.D.s in science and engineering each year. The number should swell to 13,000 by 1970 in order to meet the anticipated demands of industry, government, and education. By that time the United States should number in its census about 2.5 million professional scientists and engineers; about 170,000 should have their doctorates. This means that by 1970 about one person for every five hundred employed will have a Ph.D. degree in science and engineering. The new Ph.D.s will have an importance in the nation's economy far out of proportion to their numbers. They represent the kernels of creativity and innovation from which

spring new ideas, techniques, and products. A nation, used to rely-
ing upon exploitation of its physical resources of coal, oil and
minerals, or soil fertility, must learn to mine its intellectual
resources. These are not unlimited, as the bell shape of the I.Q.
curve demonstrates, and in the new age of technology it is the tail
of the I.Q. curve that is highly significant. Roughly speaking, the
top 3 per cent of the people, as measured on an I.Q. curve, constitute the core group of technological innovators, who in this
modern time must earn a Ph.D. in science or engineering.

Some communities like Dallas, Texas, have already sensed that
Ph.D.s are the key to the future and they have launched ambitious
campaigns to attract technological talent to their area. By 1963 the
Dallas–Fort Worth area boasted of more than 1,000 Ph.D.s and
plans have been announced to amass a total of 2,500 Ph.D.s by
1970. This great accumulation of brainpower is tuned to science-
based industries in which one Ph.D. is needed for every one hundred workers in the labor force. Localities that look to their future
will not only draw to their environment the best brains available,
they will also take a longer view of the situation and create centers
of learning to foster the new Ph.D.s which they desire. On the
other hand, communities living off the past, especially those depending upon tillage of the soil or on mining or forestry, will suffer
a drain on brainpower and put themselves at a disadvantage. Government R & D contracts and new industry are attracted to concentrations of brainpower; such have been the examples of Boston, San
Francisco, and Los Angeles.

The brain-drain situation has not yet reached an acute stage for
many states, and those in control of state education and politics
have not yet understood the need for "conservation of intellect." A
state like Oregon, for example, has some fine educational institutions but the state legislature is out of step with the times and cuts
back funds for research and graduate education. Perhaps the federal
government may have to step in and apply a "matching funds"
program of aid to stimulate states to develop their own research
brainpower. This may go against the grain of states-righters, but
the federal highway program has been a success, and it is reason-

able to assume that some support formula might be worked out which would even out the present disparity in research capabilities of the various states.

Failure of the government to help the states develop their own capabilities may result in pockets of intellectual poverty and aggravate their economic plight. There seems to be little doubt that industry of tomorrow follows the research path of today. Almost half of the pharmaceuticals and prescriptions filled at drugstores were unnamed five or six years ago. The postwar boom of the Du Pont Corporation had its origins in years of painstaking chemical research on nylon. A number of U.S. companies made fortunes in the postwar electronics boom making transistors, microwave devices, and a hundred new products which came from the research laboratory. With the rise of government spending on research and development, fewer and fewer companies committed their corporate funds to R & D; as a result private enterprise spends only about $1 for every $3 that the government devotes to research and development. This raises many fundamental questions about the nature of private enterprise against a background of massive federal support for R & D; these are, however, beyond the bounds of this book.

The scientists who put their minds to weapons during the war flexed their muscles in the atmosphere of power and money; they could not return to the lone-wolf research and shoestring budgets of prewar days. The elixir of federal funds had proved tantalizing and the researchers were soon back in Washington, knocking on the door of various agencies, seeking funds to buy research equipment, to build new accelerators, and to support investigations in the field of pure science.

Soon colleges and universities lined up to request research support. Nevertheless, it took some years before a National Science Foundation (NSF) was established. The Science Foundation had been conceived by Vannevar Bush as a postwar agency for fostering scientific research of a fundamental nature so that the momentum of science would not be lost in shifting from war to peace. There was general support for a National Science Foundation but the scientific community could not match the inspired campaign of the atomic scientists for their AEC.

The Congress was in no hurry to create a National Science Foundation but it did pass a bill authorizing such an agency in 1947. Vetoed by President Harry S Truman, the measure was debated for three years and finally in May, 1950, an Act was passed. The long delay in establishing the Foundation reflected in part the congressional inability to understand basic research; it reacted to the advent of atomic energy because of its obvious sensation. But to many legislators, pure research seemed unreal and unworthy of support with government funds. Matters were complicated by a squabble over policy on support of medical research. Thus when the new agency was born it was a much fretted-over infant. Unlike the AEC, which inherited the resources of the Manhattan Project, the Science Foundation had to start from scratch.

A month after NSF was created the Korean War broke out and this probably saved the new agency from being stillborn. The impetus of the emergency proved to be a great stimulus to research and development and naturally the Foundation shared part of the funds which Congress voted for the revitalization of U.S. science. Even so, NSF was slow to prosper; it took five years before its annual budget exceeded $10 million. It can be argued that this snail-like pace was because of NSF's regard for the hostility of Congress or, more realistically, it can be attributed to the lack of imagination and aggressiveness at the top of the NSF administrative command. Scientists looked elsewhere for big money and they received it from the AEC, the Defense Department, or the National Institutes of Health.

In 1950 Korea proved to be the take-off point for U.S. research and development; thereafter, government funds for R & D zoomed upward at a dizzy rate. Government spending for this purpose ran about $1 billion in 1950 and soared to $8 billion at the end of the fifties. The latter figure includes expenditures for all research and development; the outlays for basic science were slightly less than $1 billion for 1960.

If there are practical rewards for society in its nurture of science, there are also dangers for science. There are the hazards of bigness. Force-feeding of research may inhibit its sense of vitality. The strings which go with government funds and the red tape of contractual matters may ensnarl scientists and turn them into paperpushers and sterile administrators. When control of science funds is centered in Washington there is the ever present enigma of bureaucratic bungling, not lessened by activities of scientific types who turn to administrative posts for a variety of reasons. Few of these science administrators retain any creative spark or even keep abreast of science. They become exceedingly adept at the politics of science, however, and learn to make policy and assign contracts with a keen eye for agency interest and the favor of influential men in government. One wonders if a Galileo or an Einstein might win a research contract if he were to apply to the National Science Foundation today.

President Eisenhower took note of the phenomenon of exploding science in his farewell message to the nation, January 17, 1961:

Today, the solitary inventor, tinkering in his shop, has been overshadowed by task forces of scientists in laboratories and testing fields. In the same fashion, the free university, historically the fountainhead of free ideas and scientific discovery, has experienced a revolution in the conduct of research. Partly because of the huge costs involved, a government contract becomes virtually a substitute for intellectual curiosity. For every old blackboard there are now hundreds of electronics computers.

These were biting words from a man who rarely used them in public, but he added an even more ominous warning: "The prospect of domination of the nation's scholars by federal employment, project allocations, and the power of money is ever present—and is gravely to be regarded."

Big science has become an institution in the United States; this is taken for granted, but many scientists are concerned because big science is not necessarily great science. The two adjectives are often used interchangeably so perhaps some substitution of terms is advisable. Scientists are worried that massive science, bloated on federal funds, may not turn out excellent science. Quantity and quality should not be confused and in science nothing is so important as quality.

President Lyndon B. Johnson has emphasized the need for the United States to become a Great Society. However one may characterize such a society, great science is essential to it. This is not just because such science bears rich technological rewards in material benefits, but also because of the intellectual invigoration which springs from truly creative science. Science has grown big in the United States primarily because of its payoff to society—because of the practical benefits which flow from its applications. Science for the sake of science—which is what makes science great—takes up one-tenth of the total U.S. funds devoted to research and development, and this is a charitable overestimate.

UNIVERSITY, LABORATORY, "THINK" FACTORY

2

Was Eisenhower's worry, that big government might capture big science and indenture it, justified? How did the scientists themselves feel about it or were they so captive that they could not voice their doubts? Would a group so poorly organized as the scientists prove to be an easy prey to a massive envelopment movement by bureaucracy, backed up by the reserve strength of the U.S. Treasury?

It is rather curious and perhaps suggestive that the scientists who debated President Eisenhower's message publicly were largely not in the universities. Dr. Alvin Weinberg, director of the AEC's Oak Ridge National Laboratory, had this to say:

> I think there is a very grave danger to our universities in this incursion of big science. A professor of science is chosen because he is extremely well qualified as a scientist, as a thinker, or as a teacher; once big science has invaded his precincts and he becomes an operator (even though a very effective one), his students and his intellectual eminence and proficiency are bound to suffer. I do believe that big science can ruin our universities, by diverting the universities from their primary purpose and by converting our university professors into administrators, housekeepers and publicists.

Dr. Philip Abelson, director of the Geophysical Laboratory of the Carnegie Institution, did not mince words either: "Government money has been the Frankenstein of big science, and in many instances, the monster has invaded the universities." A sample indication of the extent of this invasion is given by Dr. Bentley Glass, professor of biology at Johns Hopkins University. He points out that at the end of World War II the department budget ran about $70,000 and by 1960 it was well over $1,000,000. Dr. Glass recalls his own apprenticeship as an assistant professor when he had no special funds for research and could tap the department's budget for no more than $100 annually. Describing the typical researcher, "He made all his own media, did his own sterilizing in a Sears Roebuck pressure cooker, kept his own stocks without assistance, and was grateful for some help in washing up the glassware." Jumping from Dr. Glass's laboratory in Baltimore to the campus of Stanford University in California, we can perceive the change if we only fly over the institution. The campus is transformed by a two-mile-long high-energy accelerator being built at a cost of $120 million; it will cost over $200 million to pay for operations and research with this landscape-modifying machine during the next decade.

After the war, scientists found themselves in an interlude of decision. Many had been uprooted from their previous posts, principally academic, and they shifted about for a time looking for greener pastures. Some liked the bigness of research in places like Los Alamos, but most of the big-name scientists at the weapons laboratory did not wait for an Atomic Energy Commission to be established; they returned to their universities or accepted positions in industry. Scientists at the Metallurgical Laboratory in Chicago were less anxious to put down new roots; they enjoyed a metropolitan location and an academic setting as well as good research facilities. Many were keenly intent on taming the atom's power for the production of electricity. After considerable confusion caused by delay in passing an Atomic Energy Act, the Metallurgical Laboratory was transformed into the Argonne National Laboratory with headquarters on the outskirts of Chicago, administered by the

University of Chicago for a combine of twenty-four midwestern universities which cooperated in its use. Nine northeastern universities got together to form the Associated Universities, Inc., operator of a new national laboratory at Camp Upton, Long Island. Known as the Brookhaven National Laboratory, it concentrated on fundamental research, whereas Argonne directed much of its effort toward developing new reactors for producing power. At the Clinton Laboratories in Tennessee, a third facility known as the Oak Ridge National Laboratory was established in the summer of 1946.

The national laboratories were something new under the government's patronage of science. Many scientists found them to be an answer to their prayers; they were free to do research without shouldering any responsibility for teaching. At the same time, their close ties with universities gave them prestige and the kind of atmosphere which they cherished—for them, it was the "best of all possible worlds." Some of the scientists who were most outspoken on the affairs of science as they related to the nation found haven in the national laboratories and they continued to exhibit a strong sense of social responsibility. The laboratories themselves did not assume any collective responsibility for bridging the gap between the scientist and the lay world. They did not consider it part of their mission, but they tolerated the few individuals in their organization who spoke out on public issues. Will the mammoth apparatus at the universities and laboratories contribute proportionately to great science? No one really knows, but the number of nuclear accelerators built with government funds since the war is impressive. Some have not contributed great discoveries and some are now positively in the "white elephant" category, but cannot be abandoned without severe embarrassment to their promoters and to the detriment of new proposals. At one eastern university a giant accelerator is kept running with routine research and a monotony of lusterless experiments.

The bigness of science today is illustrated by the federal expenditures in support of basic research for 1965:

National Aeronautics and Space Administration	$0.8	billion
Atomic Energy Commission	0.3	
Health, Education, and Welfare	0.25	
Department of Defense	0.2	
National Science Foundation	0.2	
All other government agencies	0.25	
Total U.S. funds for basic research	$2.0	billion

Looking at this total, one recalls the awe with which the public greeted the announcement of the wartime A-bomb project and its "fantastic" cost of $2 billion. Now this much is spent each year for basic research and eight times as much annually for all research and development.

Two billion dollars per annum is surely adequate for the support of basic science, even if one takes a lofty view of how great a society the United States should be. The real question is how the total sum is allocated to the various fields of scientific research and whether the granting agencies support research in the healthiest possible manner. Before the advent of the Space Age, the bulk of research funds was funneled into security channels—primarily to the Defense Department and to the Atomic Energy Commission. Basic research was funded largely because of a defense-minded Congress, which haggled over National Science Foundation appropriations, but glossed over funds for the AEC or for defense. The national program in basic science was therefore an accommodation to political realities.

Few scientists, even in the heady days following the war's end, would have predicted federal outlays of $2 billion per year by 1965. Fewer still would have ventured a judgment that two-fifths of this amount would be devoted to space research. Virtually no federal funds went into such research until October, 1957, when Sputnik I led to the creation of the National Aeronautics and Space Administration (NASA) and a space race. This sudden rise in research spending was clearly not attributable to any planning by U.S. scientists; it was a response which came as a result of Soviet space triumphs and a political decision to match these accomplishments for prestige purposes.

The distribution of some $2 billion to U.S. laboratories is a highly involved proposition. The lion's share goes into educational institutions and their affiliated research facilities, based upon research proposals submitted by individuals or departments of the colleges and universities. Of course, research is carried out in government laboratories or on sites under contract to the government. Other funds flow to nonprofit institutions and to private industrial laboratories.

A scientist who wishes to obtain support for work he plans to do can ask his superiors to aid in drafting a proposal to the agency of government most likely to give such assistance. If he is part of a physics department which already receives federal support the essential contacts may be in existence and the proposals handled through the department almost routinely. If the researcher comes from a small institution or if he wishes to be an "operator," he may bypass local authorities or cooperate with them superficially and visit Washington for the purpose of getting support. Various agencies have developed different procedures for handling proposals, but all have some type of review to which the project is subjected. Some may be rejected by the agency official on the basis of his own appraisal of the proposal and its relation to programs supported by his agency. Others may be studied and then farmed out to a panel of experts or consultants for their opinion of the proposed research and for an assessment of the capability of the applicant.

In this shuffling of proposals the biggest schools have an obvious advantage. The top ten research-funded universities received early in the sixties 38 per cent of all federal support given to educational institutions. These also accounted for 37 per cent of all the advisers used by government agencies to review research proposals; 759 of a total of 2,062 advisers came from ten universities. It is to be expected that the quality of scientists in the largest institutions is a cut or two higher than those from smaller institutions and that this review system tends to concentrate contract awards in the biggest schools. Furthermore, many of the new proposals may involve young Ph.D. scientists who are very much in their creative "best years." These men prefer the lush environment of large universities to the heavy teaching loads and poor facilities of smaller schools.

Thus the upper crust of the nation's universities tends to get thicker and richer.

The flood of federal research funds has washed heavily upon the campus of many a major American university as the following schedule for fiscal year 1960 (the most recent one available with pertinent detail) illustrates: (A) total operating and capital expenditures for the university and (B) total federal funds supplied to the university.

Institution	(A)	(B)	(B/A)
Michigan	$73.8 million	$22.8 million	31 per cent
M.I.T.	30.8	16.3	55
Stanford	35.1	15.6	45
Harvard	64.4	15.0	23
Chicago	52.1	12.1	23
California (Berkeley)	53.0	11.1	21
UCLA	54.2	9.7	18
Cornell	63.8	23.8	37
Princeton	15.9	6.0	38

These figures do not include obligations which institutions like Chicago and M.I.T. retain for administration and operation of huge separate laboratories. In the case of Harvard, where the federal funds account for about one-fourth of the total budget, these funds constitute 55 per cent of the support for the School of Public Health and 57 per cent of the funds for the medical school. A Harvard study revealed: "By 1960 Harvard was participating in at least 34 categories of programs managed by two score Federal agencies, under the general oversight of a dozen congressional committees."

The multiplicity of granting agencies had one real virtue. It prevented all federal funds from gushing out of a single spout under the control of a single agency or person. Thus it made less likely some ill-advised action that could cut off funds to a vital field of research. A scientist refused support from one agency might find it in another. But the system has many defects, not the least of which is that the educational institution becomes a kind of switchboard intermediary between government agencies and the laboratory. Rather than exercising critical judgment on what fields of research should be supported, the university acts as a contract office. It is somewhat at the mercy of "eager-beaver" staff members who demonstrate an ability to get contracts. There certainly are many campuses where the academic sun shines brightly upon the go-getter who lands a big government grant or who is known to be influential in this regard.

There is even a breed of scientist-carpetbagger who uses his talents and connections to line up government grants or contracts as a means of being appointed to a senior academic post for which he would not normally qualify. A scientist of little academic achievement, but well-placed in government, is thus able to head up an institute on campus because he brings a big grant to the university. Fortunately, such cases are the exception; in general the scientific community has behaved with considerable decorum and there have been no real scandals to mar the postwar record of government support of science.

Big science concentrates in the biggest institutions, as shown by the following statistics. In fiscal year 1962 a total of twenty-five institutions accounted for 59 per cent of all federal funds awarded to all schools. Ten schools (all those in the table on page 21 except Princeton, and including Minnesota and Illinois) accounted for 38 per cent of government funding of research and at the same time they turned out 31 per cent of the new Ph.D.s in science. These ten institutions also had on their staffs over half the members elected to the National Academy of Sciences. Since membership in the Academy is a hallmark of prestige, it means that such men are highly influential in recommending disposition of research funds. Everything was stacked in favor of big science coming under the domination of a few dozen universities. The top-heaviness of this situation and its obvious danger, considering the politician's geopolitical eye, seemed to occasion no alarm in scientific circles. The probable explanation for the lack of congressional interest in this lopsided allocation of government funds is that the scent of a pork barrel had not yet reached many noses on Capitol Hill. Individually, the funds were driblets compared to the amounts normally thought significant for pork-barrel politics under the old Rivers and Harbors tradition. But gradually some specific projects became multimillion dollar in scope and Congressmen began to be interested. Some scientists began to learn the names of their Congressmen and even to find their way to the House of Representatives and the Senate Office Building.

Research funds, especially those earmarked for fundamental science, have only recently been specified as such. The rule has been that research and development monies are lumped together, except in the case of the National Science Foundation where the research funds are clearly all of a fundamental nature. Research and development funds shot up rapidly in the late fifties and early sixties until they finally loomed so large that they competed with funds for other agencies—for purposes which few Congressmen could disregard since the interest on the national debt, veterans benefits, public works, and all the other functions of government had to be considered. It was at this time that the Congress began to look more closely at science and technology and to reappraise how much the government should spend on research and development.

In the House of Representatives, Emilio Daddario's subcommittee on R & D studied many aspects of science and technology and late in 1964 issued a report titled "Distribution of All Government Research and Development Funds." Funds from the Defense Department, NASA, and the AEC were listed in terms of totals for all fifty states. Of the nearly $10 billion actually contracted for in fiscal year 1963, the single state of California received $3.807 billion, which included 42 per cent of all defense R & D, 49 per cent of NASA's R & D, and 25 per cent of AEC's R & D. The top ten R & D benefiting states were:

California	$3,807 million
New York	917
Massachusetts	451
Pennsylvania	349
Texas	331
Maryland	325
Washington	321
New Jersey	288
Florida	248
Missouri	233

The lowest-ranking twenty states won R & D contracts which added up to a total of only 1 per cent of that for all fifty states. Obviously, the R & D pie cannot be sliced into fifty equal pieces; this would be the height of folly since some states have few resources suitable for such contracts. Take, for example, Wyoming or North Dakota which shared bottom place on this R & D list. Primarily agricultural states, they cannot boast of any concentration of scientists and engineers to attract the award of an R & D contract. But the United States boasts of high mobility for its workers and unless a state deliberately chooses to be at the tail end of research activity, it can act to get its "fair share" of big science and—we must add because of the engineering angle—massive technology.

Science points the way to the future for advanced industries, and those states aspiring to technological status will gradually slip into an "underdeveloped" condition unless they gear themselves to the pace of modern science.

Obviously the demands the government made upon the universities and the opportunities for fund-snaring combined to produce marked changes on the campus. Science departments swelled to remarkable proportions as the government pumped money into academic research. The demand for more Ph.D.s and federal support in their production led to the development of Ph.D. "factories." On a visit to Columbia University I asked the head of the physics department about the status of graduate students, "Are any deserving students without financial support?" The answer I received was both pleasing and disturbing. I was told that all the graduate students were well taken care of and that funds could be secured for anyone with real talent. "Aren't there any rich graduate students who want to study physics?" I asked, and all I got for an answer was a laugh. Actually, as we shall show, any government investment in a Ph.D. in science will pay itself back many times over during the course of a man's active career. But I could not help but reflect back to my own graduate days and recall the complete absence of federal funds.

The degree of involvement of the federal government with the university complex is just beginning to be known. So many intersecting lines of authority crisscross the federal funding pattern that no one could be sure just how much the universities were drawn into the web of government influence. One should not conclude that the agencies of government seduced the academicians into accepting contracts. Enterprising scientists (known as "big wheels" or "operators") shuttled back and forth to the nation's capital seeking federal aid. More than just a few university presidents extended their fund-raising to the Washington environment. And some ingenious "operators" used their influence as employees or consultants of agencies like the AEC to dicker with colleges for attractive posts. Their proposition, put in its baldest terms—and this was rarely necessary—was simple: if the institution would accept the scientist on its staff, usually in the preferred position of directing some new activity, he would in return "guarantee" to bring with him a big government contract. If this suggests a trace of corruptibility among scientists, it must be noted that they are human and endowed with all the foibles of ordinary mortals. Professor Martin Summerfield of Princeton University has pointed to danger signs in higher education, specifying one as "the inversion of the ladder of professional standing, so that a contract-getting professor tends to rank above a scholar." He has deplored, "the distortion of career aspirations of students who become convinced that the heart of research is contract negotiation, and the purpose of a research paper is to impress a sponsor."

Man has always been intrigued by the ultimate nature of things, probably ever since a nomad-philosopher watched grains of desert sand trickle through his fingers and speculated about what might be within the smallest speck of sand. A Greek thinker must have pondered, long before the days of Plato, the final nature of a liquid-like water which froze to brittle hardness and evaporated under the sun's heat in an invisible transformation—what the scientist calls a "change of state." Even the most dimwitted of humans has sensed the majesty of a starlit night when the glitter of myriad pinpoints of light displays the gaudy splendor and wondrous texture of our universe. To reverse this outlook and peer

deep within nature's atom bower is the special pleasure of the breed
of men who train themselves to see where the earthly eye stops
short. The human senses fail long before the outermost borders of
this strange territory are reached, and scientists rely upon ingenious instruments to substitute for the human grasp. Thus they perceive and believe that which no man can see. And the view which
is glimpsed is every bit as grandiose and as mystifying as the riddle
of the night sky. In this exquisite jumble of infinitesimally tiny
particles which dance in perpetual abandon there is a rhythm and
a pattern that excites the physicist to a deeper penetration of the
mystery.

Among the scientists have been the "big-machine men"—i.e.,
the scientists who devote themselves to the investigation of high-
energy physics. Ernest Lawrence of the University of California
was the inventive scientist who developed the cyclotron. During
the thirties he built bigger machines for accelerating the tiny particles of physics to higher and higher speeds; he rounded up funds
wherever he could find them—which in those days was from private sources. The use of these accelerated, high-speed particles
proved to be eye-openers for the physicists, allowing them to peer
deep within the heart of the atom.

Ironically, it takes bigger and bigger machines or accelerators
to probe deeper into the nuclear mosaic and, like all man-made
machines, these cost more and more. It was the *ad astra* price of
higher energy machines that alarmed officials of the government
and caused them to ask the scientists to forecast their plans for a
period of twenty years. Beginning in 1962, some sixty-eight scientists and federal officials began their cost projections and on April
26, 1963, they submitted a fifty-eight-page report. An assortment
of fifteen big machines was tabulated, three of which were scheduled for completion in the seventies and one in 1981; all others
were in operation or under construction. Only two were not
located on the east or west coasts—a fact which was to cause a
coalition of midwestern scientists and Congressmen to petition the
White House for a more equitable geographical distribution of the
installations. By the year 1972 the program would cost more than

$500 million each year, and the anticipated costs for the 1970–1979 decade were $5.26 billion.

This government report has not yet received much attention. Yet it raises a whole series of critical questions both for science and for democracy. Since the scientists who prepared the report are specialists, the scientific "community" is not really represented. No attempt is made in the report to relate the needs of high-energy physics to the total research needs of all science. Nor is any mechanism indicated whereby such adjudication might be arrived at; there is no Supreme Court of Scientists in the United States which might act as Solomon to hand down such a judgment. But the real question which is posed for democracy is the justification of so much public money for a single field of science. What value will our democratic society derive from such an investment of $5 billion in a single decade?

No scientist whom I know has ever maintained that high-energy physics is going to build a bigger bomb or otherwise enhance the nation's security. No physicist can foresee any direct dividends in the form of tangible benefits accruing from this national investment. There may be some marginal whirl-off effects in instrumentation, but none is foreseeable that would come close to matching the outlay of funds involved. The fact is that the high-energy physics venture represents a *tour de force* in pure science. Physicists are so keenly intrigued by the quest for knowledge that they believe a democratic society can afford to pay the bill for a purely intellectual expedition into the unknown.

Since the organization of scientists has no central body for planning its future—indeed, many scientists rebel at the mere mention of such forecasting—it is an amorphous body capable of being deformed from without, as in the case of the political factors and decisions which determined the U.S. space program. It is therefore capable of being deformed by internal forces as well. But will scientists other than physicists, or physicists other than the "high-energy boys," resent the power play which will put so much research money into one important but rather special field of physics?

Even though the government has been lavishly generous in supporting research, the potentialities of modern science are so vast that the outflow of funds has not kept pace with demand. When legislators called a halt to further increases in R & D funding, they naturally precipitated some consternation in the Temple of Science. Congressmen began asking hard questions. They sought justification for the various projects advanced by the scientists and they were skeptical of mounting budgets for high-energy physics. After all, they reflected, Congress has been appropriating money for big machines ever since the end of the war and the payoff is hard to explain to taxpayers. In effect they asked: "What is the value to society of high-energy physics?"

Physicists who specialized in this branch of science were quick to champion their cause. They cited the nobility of their research and the intimate grandeur of their quest into the nature of matter. As Dr. E. L. Goldwasser, professor of physics at the University of Illinois, put it: "It seems quite possible to me that in retrospect, 100 years from now, one of the greatest contributions of this period to the culture of mankind will have been its achievement of a basic understanding of the structure of matter. In the context of today's American economy and society, one per cent may be a shortsightedly small fraction of the Gross National Product to be invested in the long range future, that which lies beyond the horizon of today." The high pitch of such a justification rarely resonates with the politician today who is enjoined by the harshness of office-holding to think in terms of practical matters on a short-term time focus. The cultural value of "beyond the horizon" research may have little meaning to his constituents.

The congressional crack-down on research funds split the high priests of science into warring factions. To many in this select community it seemed that the high-energy priesthood was attempting to take over the Establishment. Inevitably, the scientists began to question the value of high-energy physics to science. As it turned out science had been flying so high since the war that it had little time to develop its own sociology. Although it seemed that all the priests worshiped the same God of Knowledge, there was division and dissension. Those who questioned the pre-eminence of high-energy physics were given dark looks and accused of heresy. Priests who were adept at prescribing policy for the nation found themselves unable to agree among themselves on internal science policy. The architecture of the temple was at last in dispute.

We are raising here a question of science policy—of profiling the U.S. research funds so that the figure of science is in the greatest interest of science and also democracy. Here many a scientist throws up his hands. "You can't predict a breakthrough!" he will exclaim, pointing to H. J. Muller's success in genetic mutation through the use of radiation, to Harold Urey's surprising discovery of heavy hydrogen, and to the Hahn-Strassmann experiment on nuclear fission. In 1932 when Urey made his epochal experiments on hydrogen and found an entirely new form called deuterium, he never expected that it would have value other than as a sort of laboratory curiosity—yet it became a critical ingredient of the H-bomb and changed the world in which we live. Will a democratic society be wise enough or lucky enough to put its research money on the long shots and support the Mullers and the Ureys of the future? Or is it possible that big science will become the victim of sheer size and bog down, dinosaurlike, in a swampland of its own making?

No one—not even the most brilliant scientist alive today—really knows where science is taking us. We are aboard a train which is gathering speed, racing down a track on which there are an unknown number of switches leading to unknown destinations. No single scientist is in the engine cab and there may be demons at the switch. Most of society is in the caboose looking backward. Some passengers, fearful that they have boarded an express train to hell, want to jump off before it's too late. That option, it would appear, is no longer open to them, but at least the passengers can discuss the matter among themselves and attempt to communicate with those up front. Hopefully, those in command may carry on a dialogue among themselves and keep a hand on the brake.

This scary picture of science and society may be overdrawn, but I think not. I believe that the proper control of science represents a truly complex enigma for our society. The basic reason for this is that while the practical applications—the hard technology which makes its impact upon the citizen—seem the most likely candidates for control, the gap between science and technology diminishes every day. By the time the necessity for the control of the technology becomes apparent the problem may be too advanced for adequate solution.

The bigness of science and the massiveness of the appropriations for it raise a special issue for scientists in relation to Congress. For example, when NASA appropriations for fiscal year 1965 came up for hearings, witnesses who appeared were professional scientists on the payroll of the space agency. Such experts, although in the main well qualified, are not lacking in self-interest, nor are they without supervisory restraints to toe the agency line. Congressmen may assume that witnesses from government agencies are uncorrupted, but they would get much less parochial testimony if they listened to independent scientists. The latter, however, appear only rarely before congressional committees; very few scientists are sufficiently informed to know when their advice would be timely. The linkages between Capitol Hill and the nonagency scientists are few and far between. Dr. Philip Abelson commented on the role of the independent critic who appears before a congressional hearing: "The witness in questioning the wisdom of the establishment pays a price and incurs hazards. He is diverted from his professional activities. He stirs the enmity of powerful foes. He fears that reprisals may extend beyond him to his institution. Perhaps he fears shadows, but in a day when almost all research institutions are highly dependent on federal funds, prudence seems to dictate silence."

Dr. Abelson's comments, which appeared as a *Science* editorial, are to be given even greater weight because as editor of the magazine which is so much a part of the establishment he frequently jabs when he would prefer to swing with a haymaker. Anyone who takes the trouble to dig through congressional hearings—and this is a chore that takes me many hours each week and fills a dozen bookshelves with reading material—cannot help but note how infrequently an independent scientist speaks his mind before a legislative group. The frequency of such contrariness is so rare as to be no more than one event per year. In fact, the instances imbed themselves in my memory permanently. One such standout was the caustic testimony of Dr. Merle Tuve before a House committee investigating civil defense. At the time Dr. Tuve headed up one of the National Academy of Sciences' many committees which, incidentally, was funded by the Federal Civil Defense Administration (FCDA). A free-wheeling individual, Dr. Tuve gave the civil defense people unshirted castigation in his testimony. Stunned by the attack, the FCDA administrator conferred with Dr. Detlev Bronk, then head of the Academy, and very soon Dr. Tuve was dropped as chairman of the advisory committee and replaced by a mild-mannered scientist, Dr. Lauriston Taylor from the National Bureau of Standards. Dr. Tuve himself was glad to be relieved of the responsibility, but it illustrates how welcome a critic can be when he speaks too frankly.

The position in which an agency scientist or consultant finds himself when facing a congressional committee is not an enviable one. As a scientist he is expected to be incorruptible, to speak the truth as objectively as his tongue can do so, but as an employee of an agency asking the Congress for funds he is sometimes pulled in the opposite direction. In general the situation rarely arises because the selection process whereby a man stays in a government post and rises to a position of influence guarantees that he will be well behaved on Capitol Hill. If the agency policy-makers have any doubt about a witness, he is passed over in favor of a man who will be "political" in his responses. "The growing tribe of *savants officiels* is a nuisance," wrote James R. Newman. "Too many scientists have been made captive and then stultified and corrupted by Government contracts and grants; too few are willing to confront the social and ethical consequences of their work."

I have observed instances where a witness before a congressional committee ought to have been asked if he had any conflict of interest in testifying. It seems to me that any scientist giving significant testimony ought to be required to disclose his consultative, contractual, or financial interests.

Corruption in the sense of misuse of funds for personal gain has not to my knowledge been practiced by scientists. Here the record of scientists has been excellent despite the huge inflow of money to scientific projects. It is quite another question as to whether scientists or administrators or politicians connected with research programs have or have not reaped financial rewards from their special knowledge of projects which the government would finance. Here the record is obscure, but we do not know that the House Armed Services Committee was sufficiently concerned about the situation to launch an investigation of conflict of interest among scientific consultants to the government. The New York *Times* called attention to the fact that prominent scientists and engineers served dual capacities as advisers to government and to industry or finance. Singled out for mention were two nationally-known scientists, one of whom served as a high-level adviser in Eisenhower's cabinet, the other was prominent in Kennedy's regime. The former served as a member of the board of directors of a national mutual fund with big holdings in defense issues. The latter distinguished himself in the field of industrial electronics and was on the advisory board of another mutual with large interests in federal research contracts. There was no indication of wrongdoing, but possible conflict of interest was raised as an issue. The *Times* reported through its Washington correspondent, John W. Finney, that "one brokerage house in Washington has unusually active accounts with some scientists employed by non-profit research groups serving the military departments."

Whether or not scientists waxed affluent as a result of misuse of their privileged access to information about impending changes in government programs or advance knowledge of contract awards, the scientists did not exactly live in sackcloth and starve during the postwar years. The campus was systematically raided until university officials found the ways and means to prop up sagging salaries and stem the professor drain. Today a physics professor in a major university can afford to live in a manner to which he was not previously accustomed.

The advent of big science could not help but have profound consequences for scientists. Since industry profited from the huge R & D contracts—and, just as significantly, did not dip into corporate funds for research—it sought out scientists as employees, as advisers, and even as members of their boards of directors. Investment firms and mutual funds noted the skyrocket take-off of certain science-based stocks and appointed scientists as consultants. At least six Nobel prize-winners were appointed to serve as board members for U.S. corporations. Big science meant big money in the late fifties and thereafter, so it was inevitable that business would involve scientists in its affairs.

Wall Street paid attention to scientists when new devices such as electronic computers and transistors moved from the laboratory stage into mass production. Investors watched glamour stocks spiral upward and put their funds into all sorts of high flyers. There was good reason to be attracted to the stock market, for solid companies like Texas Instruments shot up from $4 to $205; Litton Industries jumped from 2½ to 86 and Beckman Instruments zoomed from 13 to 159 in the span of less than nine years. But most of the glamour stocks were overvalued by overzealous investors and a day of reckoning came when the bottom fell out of this market. A big shakeout took place in electronic industries and even the giants suffered, dropping to a third of their highs. Small electronics companies dropped out of sight or were absorbed into bigger firms by merger.

Scientists as a group did not realize any disproportionate capital gains from the market boom in science stocks. No real statistics are available on this score and I am inclined to discount stories of many scientists who claimed to strike it rich. Some did, but like most investors, they talk about gains and forget to mention their "dogs" or bad investments. Many researchers who, one might think, had the "inside track" on certain market developments, never invested a penny; they were too absorbed in their work. However, quite a few scientists, especially those in applied science, were attracted to playing the market, but along with nonscientists, they were caught short by the collapse of the boom in glamour stocks.

A number of individuals in the author's acquaintance proved to be very shrewd in the business world, some in investing, others by manipulation, and a few by founding companies which prospered. Several M.I.T. scientists profited handsomely by getting in on the ground floor on two science firms. Two nationally known scientists battled it out with veteran financiers in a corporate reorganization and walked off with the better part of a million dollars. Probably the most affluent Ph.D. to found his own company and see it boom is Dr. Arnold Beckman. Once a physics instructor at the California Institute of Technology, he began making instruments and did it so well that he outgrew his Pasadena headquarters and moved to a huge new plant at Fullerton, California. At one time I estimated Dr. Beckman's capital worth as being in excess of $60 million. Edwin Land accumulated a great fortune through his pioneering of the Polaroid camera. The stock of the Polaroid Corporation remained at $2 a share from 1948 to 1952 and then it started a steady climb until it leveled off at $200 early in 1960—a hundredfold increase in price in seven years. These are not the only scientist-millionaires, but most of the scientists who earn Nobel prizes are not Cadillac-minded. One Nobel prize-winner of my acquaintance bought nothing but Fords prior to winning the prize, and then splurged on a Buick.

Scientists in their creative years seem to be motivated more by a quest for discovery (and the fame which it may bring) than by monetary gains. They do not disdain fair income, but it is not for them an end in itself or a status symbol in their community. Many scientists, however, tend to be quite naïve about their value to industry—a naïveté which industry would prefer not to have dissipated, lest their consulting fees escalate accordingly. Almost all scientists engage in some kind of consulting work, more often for government than for industry, and they tend to set a low price for their time. Some do not even inquire what fees they will be paid but leave this up to the firm. I have even known outstanding scientists who made signed agreements without any remuneration, stating that their consulting services would be available in the event the company managed to land a defense or NASA contract. The firms which negotiate with government for a contract use these unpaid scientists in order to secure the work, knowing full well that scientific competence plays a large part in the contract award.

There is a hybrid type of company which grew up in the postwar era largely as a result of defense needs—the so-called "nonprofit" organizations, sometimes known as "think" factories, which were created to serve a purpose that neither universities nor commercial firms could fulfill. Included in this category are organizations like Analytic Services, Inc., Aerospace Corporation, MITRE, Institute of Defense Analyses, RAND Corporation, and System Development Corporation. Such corporations have a structure not unlike that of a profit-making company; they have boards of directors, presidents, etc., but they are not publicly held. Not unlike some companies, the boards of directors have interlocking membership. In one case, I found that one man was on the board of five different nonprofit organizations, along with college presidents and professors.

Although the companies are called "nonprofit," they demonstrate all the eagerness of a profit-minded company in expansion and in getting new business. And they compete, sometimes with a decided advantage because of their status, with private enterprise in getting government contracts. Their pay scales compare favorably with industry and often eclipse university levels. For example, the RAND Corporation has about 250 people on its technical staff who are paid more than $15,000 per year; 65 scientists and engineers make more than $20,000 and enjoy many fringe benefits—some even have deferred annuities. The Aerospace Corporation has a technical staff of over 600 who receive upwards of $15,000 per annum, and 134 of these get more than $20,000. In the upper echelons, the scientist-president gets $75,000, the senior vice-president $50,000, and five other vice-presidents make from $30,000 to $45,000. The Institute of Defense Analyses, which employs professors on leave from their institutions, maintains a technical staff of more than 100 scientists, 54 of whom make more than $20,000 per year. Since the "nonprofits" contract extensively, sometimes exclusively, with government they serve to provide scientists with salary scales which are unattainable within federal agencies.

Although the nonprofit companies represent end runs around government salary restrictions, they do serve the useful purpose of acting as buffer between government and the academic world. By acting as separate entities, even though some are associated with educational institutions, they tend to insulate the academic community from traumatic intrusions of a military or technological project nature. They also have the virtue that they seal off an area of secret research which might otherwise tend to clog the free flow of information in academic circles. There are however very real disadvantages to the nonprofits like RAND because in their isolation they set their own standards and can easily form a self-centered community, especially since most of its work is done for the military and is thus in a measure hidden from critical judgment. However, some RAND "thinkers" are now infiltrating the university campus and taking academic posts, especially in the field of social science. This back-diffusion can be harmful, even though one might expect the academic process to eliminate the intellectual misfits, because the ex-RAND men bring with them the stamp and stigma of classified data. Thus they enjoy a privileged area of argument and can always retreat to a sanctuary of secret dataland. This can only confuse and ultimately contaminate the academic community—and interfere with the normal mode of communication by which the pure thinkers give their intellectual values to our society.

If the nonprofits like RAND, Aerospace Corporation, System Development Corporation, Institute of Defense Analyses, Analytic Services, Inc., MITRE, and others do pose something of a problem for the purity and salary scales of universities, the latter have implicated themselves quite thoroughly in the mess. When I looked up the directors of these assorted corporations, I found that college and university presidents and professors were in abundance. The subject lies beyond the covers of this book, but the democratic society would do well to examine the niche which these nonprofits should occupy in our democracy. Their relationship to the university should be studied to make sure that our society preserves the full value of independent thought which in the past flourished so well on the campus. The government has the responsibility to be sure that it does not plunder the rich resources of our nation's thinkers and corrupt their bastions of independence.

The more university scholars become victimized by big science and all of its trappings, the more they concern themselves with corporate affairs, the more will they tend to close the channels of communication which should permit unimpeded traffic from the universities to the whole of our society. As science has grown bigger, there has been no comparable growth in evidence of social responsibility. The National Science Foundation had studiously avoided coming to grips with the social consequences of the mushroom rise of science in America. Thoughtful scientists like Dr. Alvin Weinberg were perturbed by the bigness and affluence of science. And old-timers like Vannevar Bush worried about waste. "If you pour enough money into research," averred the veteran administrator, "you are bound to support the trivial and the mediocre." With some $2 billion of federal funds infusing the research activity of this country, one might have expected massive triviality and mediocrity. Undoubtedly, there has been much spinning of wheels, but research is by its very nature an inefficient process. The remarkable aspect of science, despite all that might seem indicated to the contrary, has been its vitality in the era of "overfeeding." Although $2 billion is a lot of money, we shall see the real expense is not science but technology, not research but development, not investigation but application.

The freedom of science was not placed in eclipse during the first two decades of the postwar era. Despite the ominousness of much that could cast science into the shadows, the government maintained a fairly healthy respect for science (if not always for scientists). The passion of scientists for science was a unifying and uncommonly strong bond which kept even the bigness of government and industry at bay. It was tantamount to religious zeal and the new priesthood invoked it whenever there was occasion to close ranks. But no group could be so tightly bound by self-discipline that it could withstand the impact of such funds as the federal government provided to science in the first two decades following the war. Its involvement with the national defense, for example, was the primary basis for endowing the new priesthood with the substance of power. But because of the classified nature of much defense work the scientific community was split into two broad groups—those with access to military secrets and those who did not deal with classified material.

Technological spectaculars and the pyrotechnics of the Cold War highlighted the stage upon which the high potentates of science rose to power. Without the sense of urgency imparted by the opposition of East and West it is highly doubtful that the U.S. government would have supported research and development to the extent which it did. Scientists held the keys to the nuclear-missile arsenal and, as it also happened, they were the instruments to the future. No nation mindful of its prestige and influence could afford to turn its back on the new priesthood which came to initial power in the crucible of war and then won its way to affluence as the nation sought security through weapon power.

What manner of men were these strangers who moved un-observed by the public into government during World War II and emerged thereafter in the robes of the new elite? Perhaps the best description is provided by tracing their wartime evolution, their engagement with power, and their postwar behavior. This we shall proceed to do by relating how they came to power and how they sought to use this newfound strength.

3

THE RISE
TO
POWER

Before World War II there were few scientists who broke into print or in any way invaded the conscience of the layman. The scientist was pictured as a queer sort of chap who lived a hermit-like existence, dedicated to goals not much different from those of the alchemist of medieval times. I can recall the personal reactions I encountered in the thirties upon being introduced as a "physicist" (most people had never heard the word and had trouble pronouncing it). My proud announcement that I was studying "cosmic rays" evoked head-shaking and puzzled smiles.

One has to have experienced these lean years in science to remember how frugally money was hoarded for research in physics. In those days no scientist ventured to ask the federal government for funds. He gathered together what money he needed from private sources or earned extra pay as a consultant to pay for his own research. But mostly he acted as a Jack-of-all-trades and built his own equipment. Graduate students were required to take machine-shop practice and learn glass blowing. If he needed Geiger counters he made them himself, and he wired his own electronic circuits. The physicist was the original "do-it-yourself" man on campus.

Prior to Pearl Harbor few people imagined that these characters poking about the laboratory would ever amount to much. It seemed to those who took the trouble to observe them that they lived in another world remote from that of the ordinary person. As Walter Bagehot said of modern science: ". . . it is the produce of men whom their contemporaries thought dreamers—who were laughed at for caring what did not concern them—who as the proverb went, 'walked into a well from looking at the stars'—who were believed useless, if any such could be."

Laymen found it exceedingly difficult to comprehend why a scientist should be so devoted to his science, to understand the rewards of scientific search, so well described by Oppenheimer ". . . we know, all of us, that the experience of scientific discovery is a good and beautiful experience, and an unforgettable one. We know that this is true even of little discoveries, and we understand that with great ones, it is shattering." The single word "discovery" summed it up. But discovery was about the only reward.

Scientists did not appear to the public as men whose affairs made much difference in the practical world. American science was feeding on the nourishment of its European tradition; at the time of the Great Depression it had not yet overcome its own sense of inferiority. It could not command the respect of a nation sorely beset with economic difficulties, and not even the imaginative Franklin D. Roosevelt looked to science for salvation. Public monies spent on research and development were largely devoted to agricultural pursuits. When scientists found, as they did after the great crash on Wall Street, that new ideas demanded financial support for their exploitation, they did not think of asking the government to help. Funds to build cyclotrons and other expensive machinery of science were secured from private sources, generally from foundations, and the cost of operations was assumed by colleges, universities, and a few institutes.

Scientists spoke in so specialized a tongue that translation by the press was necessary to make scientific events understandable in the lay world. Yet the press took relatively little note of science in the twenties and thirties. Few newspapers could boast of employing a reporter whose full time was devoted to covering a science beat. News editors took little notice of scientists. It was exceedingly difficult to make news from the substance of science in those days. Occasionally a U.S. scientist distinguished himself by winning a Nobel Prize, as did Arthur Compton in 1927, and the event was worthy of press coverage. Reporting on the discovery which made Compton famous was quite another thing; it was so far from the public experience and educational background that it seemed futile to explain. Nor was there any real drama in a scientist who measured things with odd-looking equipment in a musty university room. It was more newsworthy when the public could see some action—as, for example, when Arthur Compton was photographed launching strings of balloons from the University of Chicago's Stagg Field to track down the mysterious cosmic rays. Science in general was difficult to visualize and impossible to understand. Science could not compete with the glamour and visibility of events on the sports page.

From the days of Benjamin Franklin the affairs of science in America had been the business of a few societies. The growth of science was slow because the nation's economy and educational system were not oriented toward dependence upon physical research. There was little emphasis upon science in universities, and the nation depended upon Europe for much of its scientific innovation. The nation's needs were focused on products of the soil, of the mine, and of the mill. Men worked with horses, plows, and simple machines until the steam boiler came along.

Various scientific societies served the needs of geologists, biologists, and chemists. In 1847 the American Association for the Advancement of Science was born with an initial membership of 461 scientists, "designed to embrace all laborers in Physical Sciences and Natural History." It grew to national prominence but its membership climbed slowly. By the turn of the century it counted 2,000 members; 8,000 by the onset of World War I; 18,000 by 1930. It was to double this number in World War II and, in the mid-sixties, to rise to 100,000. Its individual societies tended to limit their activities to purely professional chores such as holding meetings and publishing papers. One did not find them taking an active role of social responsibility, not even later in the kind of lobbying that engaged many atomic scientists after World War II.

The National Academy of Sciences had been created by an Act of Congress in 1863 and signed into law by President Abraham Lincoln. According to the Act:

. . . the Academy, shall whenever called upon by any department of the Government, investigate, examine, experiment, and report upon any subject of science or art, the actual expense of such investigations, examinations, experiments, and reports to be paid from appropriations which may be made for the purpose, but the Academy shall receive no compensation whatever for any services to the Government of the United States.

Originally, its membership was limited to fifty scientists; today there are more than six hundred. In World War I, President Woodrow Wilson added a National Research Council to the Academy to broaden scientists' participation in the organization. But throughout most of its history the Academy has fulfilled a kind of honorific role—a Scientists' Hall of Fame. Over the years it acquired the atmosphere of a rather stuffy gentleman's club. The Academy was, furthermore, a dismal failure as ambassador for science in Congress. Strategically located on Constitution Avenue in the nation's capital, it could have established a bridge between science and Congress, but it did not.

Society's lack of concern for science, and science's lack of concern for society continued until the end of World War II.

Indicative of the times was the case of a top-flight nuclear physicist who graduated with a Ph.D. from Princeton in 1937 and found only four research jobs available to him in the entire United States. The young scientist considered himself lucky to land a position that paid $1,800 per year. He had received no government support as a student, nor did he get any financial aid for his doctoral research. Much of his research equipment was begged, borrowed, or made from scratch; very little was ordered from an industrial supplier. The reason was obvious: the universities were

limping along on a pittance. But despite the deadening impact of
the thirties, American science exhibited growing vigor. Its practitioners were passionately dedicated to research and what they
lacked in financial support they more than made up for with
ingenuity. During the Depression years American science grew
stronger and less dependent on Europe. In the first thirty years of
this century only three American physicists won the coveted Nobel
prize. If the numbers of U.S. scientists earning Ph.D. degrees
were not large, these additions to the scientific family were well
trained, imaginative, and used to hard knocks. The war years were
to prove them versatile as well. They displayed a remarkable
ability to jump into a new field and to become expert in it rapidly.
Men trained in nuclear physics found themselves doing research
on radar, on infrared systems, or on proximity fuses. Before the
war American scientists buried themselves in their research, concentrating on what is known as "basic" or "pure" or "fundamental" science. The youthful J. Robert Oppenheimer, for
example, devoted his talents to fundamental physics—to the inter-
actions of the elementary particles of physics and to cosmic-ray
investigations. So preoccupied was he with his mental excursions
that he freely admitted years later that he never bothered to read a
newspaper. Most physicists were in fact so deeply absorbed in their
work that they failed to see the war clouds gathering over Europe.

This breed of scientist was almost entirely unknown to the public. To be sure there were occasional news stories about cyclotrons,
atom-smashing, and atoms. But if anyone gave serious thought to
the scientists who probed the mysteries of the atom there was little
to indicate it. The nation still felt the deadly ennui of the Great
Depression. Though there was no particular premium placed on
brains in society at large, the small band of nuclear physicists who
matured in the thirties attracted to itself the best intelligence in
the scientific community. Despite its economic poverty, the field of
nuclear science abounded in treasure—that is, the kind that true
scientists seek. They were as poor in dollars as anyone else, but
they found in their researches the greatest of rewards: new discoveries. United States science began to come into its own when,

in institutions like the California Institute of Technology, the University of Chicago, Columbia University, the University of California, and the Massachusetts Institute of Technology (M.I.T.), as well as a dozen others, discoveries of first rank were made by lone researchers or by small teams of scientists, often a professor aided by a graduate student, working on a shoestring budget. For the most part, physicists made their own equipment; every Physics Department had its own shop where the physicists worked side by side with machinists.

Roosevelt's New Deal never tapped the enormous potential of the scientific community. It is true that Henry Wallace as Secretary of Agriculture did win support for agricultural research and there was a measure of government aid to scholars, but these were the exceptions. For a time in 1933 it had appeared that there might be a New Deal for Science when M.I.T.'s President Karl T. Compton was invited to Washington to survey the science research needs of the country and to make recommendations. For two years Dr. Compton worked at the assignment, making proposals which were repeatedly turned down, usually by Harold Ickes. The Compton program could have been immensely valuable to the nation, but it failed to win support. Dr. Compton had the right idea, a $75 million dose of resuscitation for American science over a period of five years. It would have helped fortify U.S. science for the war effort, but Dr. Compton was frustrated by opposition and conflict within the aging membership of the National Academy of Sciences. There was practically no young blood in the organization; the average age of its members was sixty-two and a scientist under fifty was considered a youngster—only two were under forty. The National Academy of Sciences could and should have backed Compton's program to the hilt, but its members bickered over the proposals and convinced him he was wasting his time in Washington.

Scientists are individualistic and the scientific community had no real coherence; there was no single forum for articulating its views. The only organizations were those representing special-field groups like the American Physical Society or the American Chemical Society. These handled the matter of scientific publications and made provision for periodic meetings, but they did not act as a pressure group to lobby for government action or support.

The notion that the federal government should grant funds to universities for atomic research was radical in its day. Scientists were alms-takers and they did not dream of going to Uncle Sam for support. The government, by the same token, did not dream that scientific research in universities would revolutionize the conduct of war, dramatically affect the health of every man, or be crucial to the national economy. Roosevelt would probably have been bitterly attacked as a visionary if he had poured money into university research during the stultifying Depression years.

In 1939 the federal government had no specific budget for research and development. By estimate it was spending that year roughly $50 million, most of it directed to agriculture. The U.S. Navy had its Naval Research Laboratory on the Potomac River just five miles south of the White House, and the War Department did a little research in its Signal Corps and at its ordnance centers. But most scientists thought of the National Bureau of Standards when they reflected upon science in government. Hard hit by the budgetary cutbacks of the thirties, the Bureau scrimped along on $2 million a year, putting most of its efforts on rather prosaic undertakings. It concentrated on testing concrete, steel, and building materials and on work in the classical lines of physics.

Thus the federal government was far removed from the frontier of fundamental research when on March 17, 1939, Enrico Fermi briefed representatives of the U.S. Navy on the possibility that a chain reaction in uranium might release a million times more energy than any known chemical explosive. But Fermi was not one to overstate his case and, furthermore, as a foreigner newly arrived in the United States, he did not inspire the greatest confidence among the Navy's top brass. Dr. Ross Gunn of the Naval Research Laboratory did, however, become enthusiastic about the possibility of a chain reaction, and Dr. Leo Szilard, a Hungarian refugee scientist working with Fermi, appealed to Gunn for financial aid to promote uranium research at Columbia University.

Szilard, like Fermi, Eugene P. Wigner, Edward Teller, Albert Einstein, and John von Neumann, was foreign-born and like them sensitive to the ways of oppression and devoted to freedom above all else. They had found a haven in America from European persecution and were more aware than others of the dangers which threatened.

Dr. Gunn tried to convince the Navy to respond to Szilard's plea for aid, but he was forced to write on July 10, 1939, that the government had no administrative provision for such support. "It seems almost impossible . . . ," wrote the naval scientist, "to carry through any agreement that would be really helpful." The impatient Szilard was convinced that more drastic action had to be taken. At Princeton University, Szilard conferred with another physicist of Hungarian origin, the brilliant thirty-six-year-old theoretician Dr. Eugene P. Wigner. Where Szilard was apt to be dashing and arrogant, Wigner was deferential and inclined to be cautious and respectful of authority. He insisted that it was essential, despite the setback from the Navy, to seek government support. Szilard was discouraged and argued that if they went to the government agencies, "We'll get pushed around like a football." But he agreed to make another approach to the government. Typically, he could reverse course in conversation while giving no concession afterward that this had not been his idea all along. Szilard suggested that they enlist Einstein's support in a direct appeal to President Roosevelt.

It was quite natural that the two scientists should turn to Einstein. As the world's most renowned scientist, his name would command respect in the White House. Einstein himself had been an overnight guest at the White House shortly after he took up residence in the United States. Einstein's attitude toward Hitler was a matter of public record and he could be expected to listen sympathetically to a proposal which would forearm the United States with a weapon that the Germans were understood to be developing. Both Wigner and Szilard felt that the need to be first in getting the A-bomb would override Einstein's pacifistic views. There was also the fact that Einstein was a friend of Queen Elisabeth of the Belgians; this entered into the calculus of the problem because some action would have to be taken to make sure that Belgian uranium did not fall into Hitler's hands. And finally, Einstein had a parental role with respect to atomic energy; Einstein's $E = mc^2$ relating mass and energy, formulated in 1904, was the fundamental underpinning of this new energy source.

There was only one flaw in this scheme. Einstein had left Princeton for a summer near Peconic Bay on Long Island, New York. Szilard neither drove nor owned a car, so Wigner proposed driving out to Long Island in his Dodge coupé. Early on Sunday, July 30, 1939, the two Hungarian-born physicists set out from Princeton to see Einstein. That morning the New York *Times* carried a lead story in its magazine section titled "War—and the Death of a World," reminding its readers that twenty-five years ago that week the world had been plunged into war. All summer the news from Europe had been ominous and both Wigner and his companion felt an urgency to their mission. Einstein showed his two friends to a large screened-in porch which also served as a dining room. He wore only an undershirt and rolled-up unpressed pants; he was fond of informal attire. As he sometimes said, "It would be a sad situation if the bag was better than the meat wrapped in it." Though he was fond of joking and quick to laugh, Einstein that day made no attempt at levity; their mission was deadly serious. For almost an hour the three men talked. Einstein offered no objection to sending a letter to the President, but he warned, "It will be a hard thing to put this across to the military mind."

Szilard and Wigner reviewed with Einstein the recent developments in research on the chain reaction and they exchanged information on what they heard via the international grapevine about the course of German progress in the same field. A secret *Uran Verein* (Uranian Society) had been formed and research had been intensified at the Kaiser Wilhelm Institute in Berlin. They talked about the darkening war situation in Europe; it was apparent that Hitler would not be content to let matters rest with his push southward through Europe. Finally, Einstein made up his mind and began dictating a letter to President Roosevelt. The Einstein letter is reproduced below because of its historic importance.

As a matter of record, the author has attempted to reconstruct the sequence of events between Einstein's dictation of the letter and its communication to the President. Wigner recalls that he and Szilard drove back to Princeton and on the next morning, which was a Monday, his secretary transcribed the letter from Wigner's longhand notes. Wigner gave the two-page letter to Szilard, who had assured Einstein on Sunday that he would see that it got to the President. Wigner states that Szilard did not mention how this would be done, but he believes that Szilard had an economist by the name of Alexander Sachs in mind.

> Albert Einstein
> Old Grove Rd.
> Nassau Point
> Peconic, Long Island
> August 2nd, 1939

F. D. Roosevelt,
President of the United States,
White House
Washington, D.C.

Sir:

Some recent work by E. Fermi and L. Szilard, which has been communicated to me in manuscript, leads me to expect that the element uranium may be turned into a new and important source of energy in the immediate future. Certain aspects of the situation which has arisen seem to call for watchfulness and, if necessary, quick action on the part of the Administration. I believe therefore that it is my duty to bring to your attention the following facts and recommendations:

In the course of the last four months it has been made probable —through the work of Joliot in France as well as Fermi and Szilard in America—that it may become possible to set up a nuclear chain reaction in a large mass of uranium, by which vast amounts of power and large quantities of new radium-like elements would be generated. Now it appears almost certain that this could be achieved in the immediate future.

This new phenomenon would also lead to the construction of bombs, and it is conceivable—though much less certain—that extremely powerful bombs of a new type may thus be constructed. A single bomb of this type, carried by boat and exploded in a port, might very well destroy the whole port together with some of the surrounding territory. However, such bombs might very well prove to be too heavy for transportation by air.

–2–

The United States has only very poor ores of uranium in moderate quantities. There is some good ore in Canada and the former Czechoslovakia, while the most important source of uranium is Belgian Congo.

In view of this situation you may think it desirable to have some permanent contact maintained between the Administration and the group of physicists working on chain reactions in America. One possible way of achieving this might be for you to entrust with this task a person who has your confidence and who could perhaps serve in an inofficial capacity. His task might comprise the following:

a) to approach Government Departments, keep them informed of the further development, and put forward recommendations for Government action, giving particular attention to the problem of securing a supply of uranium ore for the United States;

b) to speed up the experimental work, which is at present being carried on within the limits of the budgets of University laboratories, by providing funds, if such funds be required, through his contacts with private persons who are willing to make contributions for this cause, and perhaps also by obtaining the co-operation of industrial laboratories which have the necessary equipment.

I understand that Germany has actually stopped the sale of uranium from the Czechoslovakian mines which she has taken over. That she should have taken such early action might perhaps be understood on the ground that the son of the German Under-Secretary of State, von Weizsäcker, is attached to the Kaiser-Wilhelm-Institut in Berlin where some of the American work on uranium is now being repeated.

Yours very truly,
Albert Einstein

On August 2 Szilard took another trip to see Dr. Einstein. This time another Hungarian countryman drove him; he was Edward Teller, a thirty-one-year-old professor of physics, who was lecturing that summer at Columbia University. There were several changes that Szilard wanted to make in the Wigner draft; specifically, he wanted to insert the words "almost certain" in paragraph two in place of "probable." Einstein agreed to the suggested changes and the letter was retyped on the spot.

Szilard then turned the letter over to Sachs for transmittal to the President. Somewhere along the way page one of the letter was retyped to make a clean original copy. Page two, with its misspelling of the word "unofficial" was left untouched, with Einstein's signature intact.

There can be no question that Sachs played a key role as an intermediary between the scientists and the President, a link vital to the success of the Einstein-Wigner-Szilard mission. Had Szilard merely mailed the letter to the White House, it might have been referred to the Armed Services for reply; this might have been equivalent to dropping the Einstein document in the dead-letter box. Significantly, when Szilard felt the need to communicate with government he chose to have the Einstein letter hand-carried to the President. He did not make use of the National Academy of Sciences (he was not a member); nor did he go through any other scientific channel. Szilard knew that it would be hopeless to fight upward through the echelons of government bureaucrats; he aimed instead at the top.

Szilard prepared a technical memorandum dated August 15, and Sachs prepared a covering letter. But the Einstein letter had to wait until October 11, 1939, before it reached Roosevelt's office. The President was on a sea cruise in late August. On September 1 Hitler sent his motorized might racing across Poland, and the President declared a state of limited national emergency on September 8. For a month his calendar was full. Finally, on October 11, Sachs saw Roosevelt and began to read from his dossier.

In commenting on this, Roosevelt's first encounter with the facts about fission, John Gunther notes: "Roosevelt had as much knowledge of the possibility of splitting the uranium atom to produce a chain reaction as the corner cop." Yet the Einstein letter was an impressive document even to a novice in science, and a President faced with a prospect of involvement in a growing war had to respect the promise of weapon power even though its invisible seeds were buried in the strange land of nuclear physics. Perhaps the most potent argument of all was the chilling possibility that the Nazis would put their hands on this superweapon before the United States. All three scientists who collaborated on the letter to the President had been motivated by the nightmare of Nazi domination of the world if Hitler's scientists should develop such a nuclear bomb.

Still it would have been understandable if Roosevelt had turned the dreamers aside. A Harding or a Coolidge would probably have dismissed their atomic proposal as an Alice-in-Wonderland fantasy. Roosevelt himself, despite the note of urgency in Einstein's letter and the concern about Nazi activities in the uranium field, was content to let the problem be resolved by the experts. As President he took appropriate action and shuttled the issue to the proper cubicle of the federal government, namely to the National Bureau of Standards.

Roosevelt knew very little science; nor did he have any Presidential science adviser at his hand, as has every American President since Dwight D. Eisenhower. Henry Wallace, though a scientist in his own right, was hardly equipped to advise on a specialized branch of physics. However, Roosevelt appreciated the Nazi danger in the scientist's terms and decided to have a committee of scientists, under the chairmanship of Dr. Lyman J. Briggs, director of the National Bureau of Standards, investigate the feasibility of the Einstein proposal. This was not a go-ahead for the atomic project, but it was a White House-directed motion to look into the matter carefully. As such, history marks the response to the Einstein letter as the genesis of the A-bomb. The President did send a brief reply to Albert Einstein, who was invited to attend the first meeting of the Briggs Uranium Committee on October 21, 1939.

Significantly, when Roosevelt turned the matter over to Briggs, not a single scientist in government had done any research on uranium fission, though, in the United States alone, thirty-four scientists had already worked on the problem and had published their results. Government laboratories were no hotbeds of scientific ferment and Szilard could not have been overjoyed at the thought of going to Briggs's office on October 21, 1939, to have his embryonic project assayed. To judge from an official history of these early days, published by the Atomic Energy Commission in 1962, Szilard had reason to be wary. The history characterized Briggs, who had been employed in the Department of Agriculture and the Bureau of Standards since 1896, starting his career in soil science, as "slow, conservative and methodical"; while these qualities may have been ideal for heading up the Bureau, they did not commend themselves to the rash venture which Szilard proposed.

Professor Einstein begged off attending the first meeting of Briggs's group. An army colonel and a navy commander represented the Armed Services and, in addition to Teller, Wigner, and Szilard, there was a Bureau of Standards physicist and a young nuclear expert Dr. Richard Roberts of the Carnegie Institution of Washington, who had published the first definitive article on nuclear power the month before. In his pocket was a lengthy article summarizing nuclear research. (The paper was voluntarily withheld from publication.) The physicists' talk must have perplexed the two officers, who were accustomed to artillery shells. One scientist pointed out that if a single kilogram of uranium were fully fissioned, it would release the equivalent of 20,000 tons of TNT. The army ordnance expert was unimpressed. He pointed out that he had been outside an ordnance depot one day when it blew up. "It didn't even knock me down," the colonel asserted, and he proceeded to give the group a brief lecture on how wars are won by men and morale, not by weapons. Einstein had been right in his prediction that the military would be hard to win over to this new energy source. But, as it turned out, the scientists were not asking for a stupendous amount of money—actually only $6,000 to buy a large quantity of graphite so that Enrico Fermi could study the behavior of neutrons to see if a chain reaction in uranium would be possible. Before the meeting broke up, the officers promised that the money would be made available, and thus the nation's atomic project was launched.

The scientists themselves were in the dark about the prospects for uranium as a source of power. While Szilard was enthusiastic, Fermi was more down to earth and conservative. His attitude was: wait and see what the experiments with graphite show. Basically, the scientists lacked information about the behavior of atoms, and the only way to get the answers was to plan new experiments and analyze the results. This was why Fermi needed graphite and $6,000. Thereafter the world would never be the same either for the layman or for the scientist.

Dr. Briggs had realized that nuclear fission was beyond his competence and he had wisely selected as his personal adviser Dr. Philip Abelson, who was in the forefront of atomic research and neither slow nor conservative in his work. Thus Briggs's committee had been oriented toward acting favorably upon the uranium proposal. The decision, nevertheless, could easily have gone the other way—it would have been safer to hedge on the project and review it to death. This first real encounter between science and government came off well for science. Szilard probably underestimated the power of scientists like Wigner and Teller, who attended the first meeting. These men so towered above the scientists at the Bureau that they made it difficult for a man like Briggs to turn them down. In retrospect $6,000 seems like peanuts as the start of a huge project. But the important thing was that the decision had been to go ahead. The scientists had their way—as they were to in many ensuing encounters with government.

The initial approval of the uranium research did not mean that there was to be smooth sailing thereafter. The project was too much of a departure from the government's relation to science; and the organization of science, both within government and outside it, was too ill-defined to deal aggressively with offbeat proposals. It was a murky business at best. Physicists like Fermi were groping in the dark, trying to determine whether the "nuclear constants" would permit a chain reaction to "go." Everything focused on one lone statistic—the value of "k," the reproduction factor for a chain reaction. If "k" turned out to be greater than 1, the chain reaction would "go." If not, then nature's cards were stacked against success for the uranium project.

In the winter of 1939–1940, when a small band of nuclear physicists set out to explore the possibility of a chain reaction in uranium, there were only about two-score physicists who had done research in uranium fission and perhaps only a hundred who were qualified to undertake this kind of research. The research was dispersed in university laboratories and coordinated out of Washington through the agency of the Briggs committee. Secrecy was clamped down on the project to such a degree that it hampered progress; scientists were not able to communicate freely. Things proceeded at far too slow a pace for the impatient Szilard though he had first proposed that the scientists adopt a voluntary program of secrecy to conceal the work from the eyes of the Germans. He needled Washington officials and even enlisted Einstein's support to plead for full speed ahead on the bomb project.

All sorts of technical factors made Fermi's work harder to pinpoint so far as "k" was concerned. The uranium he obtained commercially was far from pure and the graphite was riddled with impurities that fouled up exact measurements. Actually, no one knew how to make pure uranium or graphite on a commercial basis.

As Fermi and his fellow physicists labored to see how "k" would turn out, American science began to feel the impact of the war in Europe. Gradually at first and then more quickly scientists began to drift away from the campus and head for "secret" research laboratories. "Secrecy was not started by generals or security officers but by Szilard," Fermi said after the war, and explained: "He proposed to people that they go easy and keep back their results until it could be seen whether the results were dangerous to our security." This was a voluntary type of secrecy in which no government or military security officers were involved. Roberts, for example, summarized the state of nuclear knowledge in the summer of 1939 in a perceptive thirty-page article which he intended to submit for publication. However, he decided to withhold the information and

to this day it remains an original, partly typed and partly hand-
written, manuscript in his files in Washington, D.C. Roberts'
brother, an inventor-scientist, was so impressed by work on the
chain reaction that he offered to file patents on the control of the
reaction. The company for whom the inventor worked, RCA, considered the proposal and turned down the idea as "out of their
line." Thus RCA waived the basic patent on the control of a
nuclear reactor!

Scientists like Fermi had been shocked by Szilard's proposal to
keep their research secret. They were disciplined in the prompt
publication of their investigations and it seemed like a crime against
science to suppress their findings. But at the same time some sensed
that the work they were doing might find military application.
Even though the United States was not at war in 1940, Hitler's
westward push through Europe and the crumbling of defense there
convinced many U.S. scientists that they could no longer remain
neutral. Certainly they knew that it was shortsighted to hand over
to the enemy useful scientific data.

As the war clouds over Europe cast lengthening shadows and
penumbrated the United States, scientists knew that their academic
days were over. Now the laboratories had to be turned into birthing
places for weapons of war. United States scientists were not at a
loss for ideas useful to weaponry. They were, however, lacking in
the means to serve in some sort of coordinated manner for the
government. In the spring of 1940 there was no mechanism within
government for harnessing the creativity of scientists to the tasks
of making new weapons. Of course, the War and Navy departments were in existence but the quality of research in new weapons
and, as would follow, the quality of scientists doing this work was
undistinguished. The Armed Services had certain research facilities
but these were humdrum places dedicated to minor improvements
in existing armaments.

The man who stepped in at this juncture to vitalize military research was Dr. Vannevar Bush, dean of engineering at M.I.T.
through the thirties, and in 1939 president of the Carnegie Institution. He thus came to a strategic position in Washington, D.C.

Laboratories of the Institution were right at hand and they included some of the best brains in the country. The noontime meeting place for scientists was the old Cosmos Club across the park from the White House; in the club's decrepit surroundings, replete with broken springs and holes in the overstuffed chairs, Bush rubbed elbows with government policy-makers. He talked down-to-earth science with a Yankee twang that was persuasive to government administrators, Congressmen, and even to military men. From Karl Compton's merry-go-round in Washington, Dr. Bush knew that energizing the government to provide a fruitful environment for scientists would not be easy. The scientists had to be deployed in various operations where they could do the most good, and this, Bush figured, required creating a new policy and planning setup.

Bush's brainchild was the National Defense Research Committee, or NDRC as most scientists call it. It was actually patterned after the National Advisory Committee on Aeronautics (NACA) on which Bush served. It was established in June, 1940, by Roosevelt, who named Bush as chairman. The Roosevelt-Bush relationship was the first of a long chain of White House-M.I.T. linkages that was to persist for more than two decades; both the President and Bush tried to find some formula which would marry science to the military establishment, and NDRC became a year-long experiment. The scientists at the working level were concerned with administration only if it obstructed their missions or failed to give their goals sufficient priority. Money was of course important, but a much scarcer commodity was top-notch talent. Bush could decide that a certain scientist ought to work on radar, and he could be very persuasive, but scientists follow their own lights and are sometimes most obstreperous when told what to do. A case in point was that of Dr. Merle Tuve, one of the original members of the Briggs Uranium Committee. A powerhouse of a man, Tuve would have been a real force on the A-project. However, the day Goering's Luftwaffe blitzed England, Tuve made up his mind to do something about things that would help to win the war. Tuve devoted himself to developing a proximity fuse, a device that was in effect a miniature radio transmitter and receiver. Such a gadget nestled in

the tip of an antiaircraft shell might explode it a set distance from
a plane. He quickly persuaded men like Roberts, Lawrence Hafstad, and others from the Carnegie Institution to perfect this new
weapon. Tuve did not think that the A-bomb was impossible; he
simply felt that it was too far in the future.

Bush's NDRC took over administrative control of the Briggs
committee, which immediately asked NDRC for $140,000 in
funds. The Briggs group wanted $40,000 for determining the
"nuclear constants" and $100,000 for Fermi to build a scale model
of a nuclear reactor—an experiment to prove out the chain reaction.
Bush handed over $40,000 but withheld the rest of the funds.
Here one can probably find some evidence for avoidable delay in
the uranium project, as quite a few of Dr. Bush's associates became
convinced it would not pay off in time for use in a war they knew
was coming. Bush brought to his job as overseer of the U.S.
science-defense effort a strong engineering slant which liked to see
problems spelled out with a display of "hard data." But "hard
data" still eluded the nuclear scientists as 1940 drew to a close.

The winter of 1940–1941 was one of intense discontent for
Szilard and others who felt that their efforts were being frustrated.
Szilard was unhappy about the fact that the Briggs committee re-
constituted under NDRC excluded scientists of foreign birth from
a policy role. Dr. Arthur Compton, who was responsible for reviewing the status of uranium research admitted, "Up to the latter
part of 1941 my conversations with Fermi had been cautious because of security reasons." And no man in America knew more
about the chain reaction than Fermi! Furthermore, the security
measures of NDRC (Bush apparently felt that these should be
tightened up in order to placate Congress and the military) began
to irritate the free-roving Szilard.

Bush sought to remedy matters by a technique which he was to
use even more repeatedly in the postwar era. He turned the problem over to a review committee. At the same time Bush sought to
mend fences with the National Academy of Sciences whose function he had really bypassed in getting Roosevelt to set up the
NDRC. He had deliberately steered Roosevelt away from reliance

upon the National Academy of Sciences, knowing that it would not be up to assuming the responsibility of a great defense effort. His National Defense Research Council and Office of Scientific Research and Development were actually end runs around the Academy. It is true that Bush appreciated the prestige value of the Academy, and he very diplomatically avoided open conflict with the Academy; in fact, he adroitly enlisted its support, once his own position was anchored in the White House. He persuaded the Academy to appoint a committee under Nobel prize-winner Arthur H. Compton, who at the time was engaged in cosmic-ray research at the University of Chicago. Compton took on the task and made the committee's first report on May 17, 1941. Compton recommended that $350,000 be devoted to the next half year of nuclear research. On the atom's military utility, the committee was cautious but concluded that it was "unlikely that the use of nuclear fission can become of military importance within less than two years." During its first year of operation, NDRC spent only $468,000 for all scientific activities, and although Bush was adept at getting funds, he had to worry about the balance of effort for the A-work, especially in terms of scientific manpower to be assigned to the job. American physicists were already in short supply. By the time the London blitz started, two out of three U.S. physicists were engaged in some type of defense research.

Compton's report troubled Bush also because it had too scientific a tone; the NDRC chairman liked harder facts and engineering data. In addition, he was struggling to revamp the NDRC organizational structure, now encompassing a multitude of assorted projects, most of which demanded evaluation and decision on funds, manpower, and priority. There was no question in his mind that the United States would be at war soon, and it was urgently necessary to shift the machinery of science into high gear. He believed that NDRC needed to focus upon things which would help to win the war and to assign high priority to developing and engineering these weapons. Under its Executive Order from the President, NDRC acted "to coordinate, supervise, and conduct scientific research" relating to weapon development. A broader mandate was needed and Dr. Bush went to the White House in June, 1941, armed with a plan.

On June 28, 1941, Roosevelt created the Office of Scientific Research and Development (OSRD) as an arm of the Executive Office. As director of OSRD, Dr. Bush was given the authority to mobilize U.S. science. Within two weeks Bush asked the Bureau of the Budget for $10 million and with little argument he received two-thirds of his request. The Office of Scientific Research and Development was patterned after the divisional structure of its predecessor. Dr. James B. Conant, president of Harvard University, became second in command to Dr. Bush; the Briggs committee was absorbed. The secret symbol of S-1 was given to uranium research in OSRD.

While the atomic project was meandering on its far from arrow-flight trajectory, in considerable part due to the novelty of wedding science to defense, in Britain scientists had made substantial progress on their own loosely organized research. Unhampered by the fetters of secrecy, British physicists came to the conclusion early in the summer of 1941 that the A-bomb was technically feasible and that they ought to get on with the job of producing the materials for it. They were far from having precise numbers of cost estimates or time scales, but, unlike their American brothers, they had arrived at a firm conclusion. British visitors to U.S. shores soon communicated their feeling of optimism to scientists like the energetic Ernest Lawrence, the University of California physicist who did so much to develop atom-smashers. Few American scientists had Lawrence's dash and drive; once he set his mind to something, no matter how extreme, he pursued a bone-crushing course. As one of the two United States members of the National Academy of Sciences under forty, Lawrence was an *enfant terrible* in American science. One is tempted to don retrovision glasses and speculate what might have happened if Szilard had gone to Lawrence in the summer of 1939 instead of to Einstein. However, when Lawrence engaged himself with the uranium atom and its bomb potential in 1941 he proceeded on a whirlwind course. He must be credited with shaking up the National Academy of Sciences review committee which Arthur Compton chaired. Compton himself relates that it was on September 15, 1941, after a meeting with Lawrence, that he saw clearly the military potential of uranium.

A draft of the British final report recommending an all-out effort on the production of material for a nuclear weapon was available on July 1, 1941, and its content had been discussed with U.S. experts on an unofficial basis. The British conclusion on the A-bomb stimulated Dr. Lawrence, and after the meeting with Lawrence on September 15, 1941, Compton's review group urged an all-out effort on uranium research. A liaison team was dispatched to England to learn first hand what the British experts had done in their research, and Compton set about preparing a report for Bush, with hard data on time scales, costs, and plant requirements. On October 9, without waiting for Compton's report, Dr. Bush went to the White House; for the first time he was able to put numbers and amounts of material before the President; these figures derived from the British. Even though Dr. Bush promised no success, for there were still many unknowns, Roosevelt gave him a free hand to see if the bomb could be made. No decision was made on the construction-production phase of the project, but it was nonetheless a turning point. The dialogue between Roosevelt and Bush, coming almost two years after the President received Einstein's letter proposing research on the chain reaction, was critical in the history of the A-bomb.

Pearl Harbor served to make the atomic scientists working on S-1 launch a redoubled effort in the research laboratories. At the same time scientist-administrators on the project began to deal with impressive budgets; at least they contrasted strongly with those of physics departments to which they were accustomed. For example, a few weeks after Pearl Harbor, Dr. Arthur H. Compton stipulated a budget of $278,000 for his work at the University of Chicago and asked that a total of fifty-eight men be assigned to uranium research there.

By the end of May, 1942, work on S-1 had progressed so that project leaders could begin planning for the next phase, namely, construction of plants to produce the nuclear material for bombs.

President Roosevelt acted to assign responsibility for this production phase to the U. S. Army under the condition of absolute secrecy. Budgets jumped skyward and a total of $85 million was earmarked for fiscal year 1943. Formal entry of the Army took place in September of that year as General Leslie R. Groves took command of the Manhattan Engineer District, an appendage of the Corps of Engineers set up to take over the next phase of S-1.

Thus three years after Einstein, Szilard, and Wigner met to concoct a means of persuading the United States government to investigate the feasibility of developing a nuclear weapon, the project was finally on a firm basis, with plants under design and sites about to be selected for construction and production.

Szilard, surveying the history of the U.S. atomic project after the war, had the following colloquy with Senator Johnson of Colorado in 1945:

Q. When would the bomb have been dropped, or when could a bomb have been dropped had the secrecy regulations not been imposed?

A. About the spring of '44 would be my best guess, because the big delay arose from the fact that our work did not have a clear goal until the end of '41, because we did not know that amounts of fissionable material which we could produce were sufficient to make bombs.

There can be little doubt that secrecy hurt U.S. progress on the bomb. If Compton, who had been charged by Bush with responsibility for evaluating the atomic program, could not talk freely to Fermi, the leading expert on the chain reaction, one must take Szilard's contention seriously. Unfortunately there is no way to verify his further estimate that the United States could have perfected the bomb by the spring of 1944. If, as Szilard was convinced, progress had been delayed by secrecy and administrative sluggishness, it must be countered that the union of science and government on a massive scale was a new experiment for the United States. Scientists were themselves unsure of how to proceed even within the context of wartime emergency. Administrators found the project to be a great anathema, since absolute security and progress were often incompatible.

Sometimes the sheer size, cost, and tempo of their wartime endeavors awed the scientists, but mostly they took to big projects with amazing ease. Although they had been plucked from the tranquillity of university environments where they worked on shoestring budgets on a solo basis, they found that they could work in teams at a frantic pace. There were exceptions, when a lone-wolf species did not run with the pack. For example, Dr. Edward U. Condon served only a short tour of duty as associate director of the weapons laboratory at Los Alamos, New Mexico. In his letter of resignation to J. Robert Oppenheimer, the laboratory director, he explained: ". . . I found the extreme concern with security was morbidly depressing—especially the discussion about censoring mail and telephone calls, the possible militarization and complete isolation of the personnel from the outside world." In this connection Condon related to the author that at one point Oppenheimer was considered for appointment as an army colonel. (Had the scientist assumed such military rank it might have proved a valuable protective armor against the assaults made upon him a decade later.)

As the scientists found themselves "under new management" reporting to General Groves, they were at last in the hands of a decision-maker. They might gripe at times that the decisions were wrong, but indecision in the project became a thing of the past. Few of the weapons-makers found time for introspection as they worked night and day, seven days a week, at the task of producing nuclear material and developing a means to explode it as a bomb. But some found time to ponder the meaning of what they were doing and to think about the consequences of their colossal experiment in the release of energy. These few scientists, wrestling with their consciences and within the limitations of the highly secret project, sought to take on a responsibility which they could not share with their fellow citizens. Elemental power was within reach of the scientists and a few determined that they would be more than technicians serving interests of the state; they would indeed seek to influence policy on the use of the bomb and the control of the atomic force in the postwar period.

The $2 billion A-bomb project was at the time viewed with great awe. And also with some trepidation, for Roosevelt told his chief of staff Admiral William Leahy: "If it works, Congress won't investigate. If it doesn't, they won't have time to investigate anything else but this." Even with his lack of fright at big numbers, Roosevelt would have been startled by the postwar sequel to the project which he initiated. To date the atomic energy program of the United States has cost the taxpayers a total of $35 billion, thus eclipsing the wartime expenditures.

Not many scientists, however, had even dimly imagined the immensity of the power which was to derive from the seemingly useless research of the thirties. Szilard sensed this power and it was that which prompted him to propose the Einstein-to-Roosevelt communication.

The very silhouette which the atomic glare cast from Hiroshima served to focus upon the A-bomb as a vivid manifestation of the power of science. The end product A-bomb was of course important, but it was even more significant that scientific and technical resources could be mobilized to convert an idea into a reality. Korea was to revive the mobilization technique and apply it to projects more costly than the $2 billion spent on the wartime A-project. Here we find another ramification of Einstein's historic proposal; not only did it serve to usher in an era of big science, it also triggered a mass organization of technology that was to find full expression in American development of the ballistic missile and in the lunar project.

For the layman, Einstein's letter marks the origin of the atomic bomb and a threat to world security. To a lesser degree it gives promise of abundant energy resources for the future. For the scientist, it meant that the separate worlds of science and society were now joined. Science would be rapidly transformed into big science.

The public regarded the scientist with a mixture of awe and puzzlement. The works of science, exemplified by the A-bomb, radar, the proximity fuse, infrared devices, and ballistic missiles, were awesome indeed, and the layman was grateful that the new breed of weapons-maker had contributed so much to ending the war. But these developments were far from the common understanding of most Americans. The atomic scientist, to single out one species of the new order, seemed an extraordinary person. Before the war the public had rarely heard about a nuclear physicist; after Hiroshima he became a celebrity, but he was also regarded as something of a mental freak. Here was a man whose mind touched at the innermost wellsprings of nature's secrets, and the layman became inclined to view every physicist as much a genius as Einstein. They were all high priests in the Temple of Science.

Scientists returned to their old laboratories or to new posts with a very considerable bonus. Their wartime efforts had produced great improvements in electronics and in most areas of instrumentation. Now they were in position to undertake research which would have been impossible a few years earlier; the fruits of science fed back to enrich research itself. Although some fundamental research was done on a crash basis during World War II, such research had been largely a matter of urgent necessity when application-oriented projects ran into dead ends and needed a rescue operation. Much research done on the chain reaction was basic and of high quality; this was evident when the secret stamp was removed from some of the work and the scientific papers were published, but the exploits of scientists in the last war were primarily built on the fundamentals which had been accumulated during prewar years. In effect, the tree of science was shaken hard enough to dislodge its fruit, ripened or not, and the scientists knew that replenishment would be a first order of postwar business for them.

The researchers who stayed on at the national laboratories had good facilities at hand, but the men who returned to the campus lacked such largess. To a certain extent they profited by an arrangement whereby the government made war equipment available to universities, but they lacked funds. Vannevar Bush and his associates had foreseen this postwar development, but Bush's plans for a government agency to support scientific research gathered dust in Congress. The atomic scientists, to be sure, worked for and got

a civilian Atomic Energy Commission (AEC), but this was also
stalled in its formation, and even when the AEC was established,
it had special interests and did not embrace all of science.

The U.S. Navy showed the greatest sympathy to scientists, partly
because the high quality of its officers made them receptive to the
new ideas with a technical content. Once it became apparent that
the Congress was not going to act promptly in support of science,
the Office of Naval Research (ONR) stepped in to give financial
aid to research in many colleges and universities. Apprehensive that
this "military" aid might impress heavy restraints on research,
scientists were initially reluctant to apply to ONR for funds. However, the first-comers were treated most cordially and rapport was
established through the efforts of scientists like Dr. Urner Liddel
and Dr. Emanuel R. Piore. The Navy's "good conduct" led larger
numbers of researchers to apply for support and soon the ONR had
a formidable program of support for the physical sciences. There
was no requirement that the research be tied to naval applications.
For example, the ONR program included aggressive aid to cosmic-
ray research—a field for which no practical application was foreseen. The Office of Naval Research also gave funds to universities
for the construction of accelerators—cyclotrons and other machines
for producing high-energy particles of no particular value to the
Navy. Gradually as the Atomic Energy Commission found its foot-
ing, it took over some of these atomic projects from ONR.

Clearly a long-term consequence of the Einstein action on the
atom was science's profound influence on the federal budget. Just
how profound was a matter beyond the wildest imagination of any
scientist. In the postwar years the annual government outlay for
research and development was to skyrocket to $16 billion. In some
cases, as in the case of the Air Force's atomic aircraft, it would
require the expenditure of a billion dollars on one project just to
prove that it would not work.

Big science and massive technology were to have increasing
impact upon the nation by creating new industries, altering the
structure of the labor force, and imposing new educational require-

ments on millions of Americans. Subsequent chapters in this book will examine the nature of these changes and how they are likely to affect the nation in the next two decades.

In prewar days man seemed reasonably secure in his perch upon the earth. There was concern expressed about the danger of over-population (itself associated with technological progress), but it did not appear that technology was an enemy of society. However, the demands and the by-products of an accelerating technological revolution challenge man's comfortable place upon the planet. It is interesting to note that in the original Einstein letter there is reference to "large quantities of radium-like elements." The conquest of the atom involved the concomitant release of contaminants so well known today because of radioactive fallout. The worldwide dispersal of these atomic by-products created global alarm and was itself a potent factor in alerting men everywhere to the need for curtailing nuclear testing. Because of the extreme sensitivity of instruments for detecting the presence of radioactivity it was possible to trace the bomb products to the farthest corners of the globe. The bones of every earth dweller were to contain measurable quantities of strontium-90 and other bomb-born atomic fragments. Man had obviously greatly magnified his power as a nest-spoiler.

Radioactive contamination is but a single example of technological affront to the ecological calm of our planet home. Modern industrial plants spew forth into the atmosphere and into rivers and lakes incredible amounts of pollutants. Any person who has flown over the Los Angeles area or has coughed his way through the freeway system needs no reminder of the localized smog hazard in southern California. Almost every metropolitan area is now being invaded by a host of pollutants. The proper control of potentially harmful technology is becoming a major problem of society.

Before his death, Dr. John von Neumann became more and more worried about technological threats of this type. "After all," the great mathematical physicist wrote, "the crisis is due to the rapidity of progress, to the probable further acceleration thereof, and to the reaching of certain critical relationships. Specifically, the effects that we are now beginning to produce are of the same order of magnitude as that of 'the great globe itself.' Indeed, they affect the earth as an entity."

Von Neumann was concerned not only about man's careless treatment of his environment, he also envisioned his deliberate manipulation of it. He had in mind the possibility of global climate control and he warned: "We should not deceive ourselves: once such possibilities become actual, they will be exploited." No one knows how close we are to the control of climate. The problem is more complicated than that which Professor Einstein broached to Roosevelt in 1939. Even if our climate should prove resistant to man's modern ways, there is still much to worry about in von Neumann's admonition. Quite apart from the specific of climate control, there is the dictum that *technological possibilities are irresistible to man*. "They will be exploited," said von Neumann in 1955. The moon race would seem to bear him out and authenticate him as a prophet. If man *can* go to the moon, he *will*. If he *can* control climate, he *will*. In other words, when technology knocks, man opens the door. He may not even bother to look through a peephole to see what is in the offing.

TWO CULTS OF POWER

4

World War II was the cauldron in which two initially quite different potions of power were mixed. Science and the military combined to produce weapons of unimagined strength, yet the scientist, who was accustomed to pursuing truth openly, was a natural enemy of the controls and authority to which he submitted under the duress of national emergency. The military, long used to firm lines of authority and to taking orders without question, abruptly found itself working with large numbers of scientists, among whom many, especially a few outspoken physicists, were often disorderly in their working habits, contemptuous of bureaucracy, and querulous about the dictates of secrecy. Yet these natural opponents were to find themselves in uneasy alliance as the power of science revolutionized armaments and the conduct of war.

Not all scientists submitted to dominance by the military and became obedient weapons makers. Some felt a deep sense of obligation to be more than technicians; they took it upon themselves to question policy even at times when this was exceedingly difficult. The policy debate which raged within the S-1 project prior to the dropping of the first A-bomb was one such example. So was the public protest spearheaded by scientists over the control of atomic energy. So was the third public dialogue, concerning the H-bomb.

When the U.S. Army applied its traditional mode of manage-

ment to the atomic scientists, many irritations arose. At first, the
two cults of power clashed over petty matters—or at least military
men *thought* them petty. Security restrictions annoyed and frustrated the scientists. Absent-minded scientists, often working late
at night, would forget to lock papers in a SECRET file and then
be summoned back to the laboratory like naughty children and
supervised as they stowed the documents away.

But the conflict between scientists and the military was not confined to disputes over locked cabinets and secret reports. They
clashed in more serious ways, chiefly after the war, over who should
control the use of the powerful weapons science had wrought, and
what that use ought to be. The dispute began early. There were
three main sites for nuclear research: (*a*) the Clinton Laboratories
at Oak Ridge, Tennessee; (*b*) the Los Alamos Laboratory, known
as Y, on a lonely mesa near Santa Fe, New Mexico, where young
J. Robert Oppenheimer directed work on the techniques of as-
sembling nuclear material for military application, and where
many other scientists were connected with the Manhattan Project;
(*c*) the Metallurgical Laboratory (a code name) on the campus
of the University of Chicago, where Dr. Arthur Compton was
project director, and where the discussion of the use and control
of the bomb centered.

Scientists at the Metallurgical Laboratory in Chicago became the
leaders in a secret dialogue with United States officials in an attempt
to focus emphasis on the control of nuclear weapons. The focus in
this one laboratory may be traced to the fact that men like Szilard
and Wigner were on the staff. And despite security measures in
project buildings, the atmosphere on campus was conducive to
reflection on the consequences of releasing nuclear energy. Furthermore, the laboratory's prime mission had been fulfilled to a great
degree by 1944 when priority shifted to Los Alamos and to the
actual making of the bomb.

Nevertheless, it was a scientist from Denmark, Dr. Niels Bohr,
not a resident at any of these sites, who first wrote a memorandum
to President Roosevelt on July 3, 1944, analyzing the political
consequences of success in the nuclear project. His rather lengthy

memorandum centered mainly on the problems of postwar control, but he did warn: "The fact of immediate preponderance is, however, that a weapon of an unparalleled power is being created which will completely change all future conditions of warfare."

Both Bush and Conant shared Bohr's concern for international control of atomic energy. Conant was particularly worried about what should be disclosed to the world once the first A-bomb was detonated; for example, should technical data be shared with Russia? Bush communicated with Secretary of War Henry Stimson on September 19, 1944, urging that consideration be given to international control as an alternative to a nuclear arms race. Three days later Bush was called to the White House and Roosevelt asked him if the bomb should be used against Japan. The battle in Europe was going well; the great invasion had been successful and Paris had been liberated. Roosevelt apparently felt that it would not be necessary to contemplate use of the S-1 bomb against Germany.

During the first week in November, 1944, over a score of top scientists at the Metallurgical Laboratory prepared a memorandum urging official action on developing a policy among the Allies regarding the new bomb. Arthur Compton who received the report was having trouble holding the laboratory together because it had largely fulfilled its bomb mission, and General Groves maintained that he could not continue to spend money on research not directly bearing on the termination of the war. However, the Chicago laboratory constituted a reserve force to use if other sites ran into unexpected technical difficulties. It kept going and many of its scientists continued thinking and writing about the control of the atom. A leader in the group was the prescient and irrepressible Leo Szilard; he was also the biggest burr under the saddle of hard-riding General Groves.

The General took elaborate pains to keep men like Szilard from finding out what was going on at the other atomic installations. Szilard was extremely ingenious in laying his hands on information he was not supposed to have or in putting two and two together correctly. It was perfectly in character for the free-wheeling Szilard to prepare a memorandum for the President in March, 1945, and completely bypass General Groves. However, Szilard felt that he might not command the President's attention in the rush of the war effort and he traveled to Princeton to persuade Professor Einstein to attach a letter of introduction to Roosevelt. The memorandum was a lengthy one and it was presumptuous to think that the President would read it through; but it was both prophetic and provocative. For example, two paragraphs forecast that A-bombs might be prejudicial to the national security:

> Before the end of the war we shall use atomic bombs against Japan. These bombs will be much less powerful than we know could be made and which in all likelihood will be made within . . . years* yet the first bomb that is detonated over Japan will be spectacular enough to start a race in atomic armaments between us and other nations.

> In a few months Russia's war with Germany may be over. The work on uranium will then undoubtedly be given a high priority there but it will perhaps still not be carried out on a large industrial scale until we demonstrate our first atomic bomb and thus demonstrate the success of this development. For a few years after that we shall almost certainly be ahead of Russia. But even if we assume that we could keep ahead of her in this development all the time, this may neither offer us protection from attack nor necessarily give us substantial advantage in case of war . . . years from now.

There is no record that the President ever saw this memorandum. Roosevelt died at Warm Springs on April 12 and the decision to use the bomb became the burden of Harry S Truman.

Szilard was probably the first scientist-in-the-ranks to put into writing his personal anguish over the use of the A-bomb. Roosevelt's death came as a jolt to the scientists and served to crystallize their thinking about the military use of the weapon. Up to this time those who could afford the time to think about it had considered the larger issues of postwar policy, the problems of international control and domestic development of nuclear power. Whether they put the actual dropping of the bomb further from their thoughts because they had confidence in Roosevelt's judgment

---

* The vital number was deleted from this censored version of the letter. The original document remains classified.

or because of moral aversion or because it was simply not an immediate problem, it seems that the matter was not uppermost in their minds until the early spring of 1945. The author recalls attending a series of meetings in Ryerson Hall (physics building on the University of Chicago campus) while snow was still on the ground; at these sessions sometimes a dozen and at most a score of physicists and chemists discussed the problems of international control. I do not recall, however, that we entered into any talk about the use of the bomb against Japan. Nor did Szilard bring up the fact that he had sent a letter to Roosevelt.

A week after Roosevelt's death another Chicago-based scientist, Nobel prize-winner James Franck, carried the problem of the bomb and its impact a step further in officialdom. Accompanied by Compton, the sixty-three-year-old German-born chemist breakfasted with Secretary Henry Wallace. Franck expressed his concern that government officials needed to be alerted to the fact that the advent of atomic energy represented a sharp break with the past and that new thinking was required to face the future. He envisioned an atomic arms race which might someday find two adversaries in the position of two opponents confined to a small cell and each pointing a machine gun at the other. (There were to be other metaphors, such as Oppenheimer's "two scorpions in a bottle," but Franck's illustrated the point of deterrence.) Furthermore, Franck pointed out in a seven-page memo laid on the breakfast table that, bad as they were, the weapons of 1945 would grow to more fearsome proportions. The situation called for control and this in turn would require much thinking and careful planning. Although Franck's memorandum did not bring up the use of the A-bomb against Japan, it was a well-reasoned and otherwise comprehensive analysis. It contained this poignant commentary on security regulations:

These regulations become intolerable if a conflict is brought about between our conscience as citizens and human beings and our loyalty to the oath of secrecy. That is the situation in which we scientists now find ourselves. We read and hear about all the efforts which the best statesmen devote to peace planning in Dumbarton Oaks, San Francisco, etc., and we hear about plans to control industries, etc., in the aggressor states, but we know in our hearts that all these plans are obsolete, because the future war has an entirely different and a thousand times more sinister aspect than the war which is fought now. How is it possible that the statesmen are not informed that the aspect of the world and its future is entirely changed by the knowledge that atomic energy can be tapped, and how is it possible that the men who know these facts are prevented from informing the statesmen about the situation?

The architecture of the United Nations was being designed in San Francisco in the spring of 1945 and at the same time scientists were completing their work on a weapon which they knew would revolutionize the conduct of international affairs.

This paradox, however, was appreciated by project leaders like Vannevar Bush and James Conant. Bush had been trying to persuade Henry Stimson for many months that an advisory committee should be appointed to help develop policy on the bomb. Finally, in the last week of April, Stimson agreed, and after a conference with President Truman, the group was established. Called the "Interim Committee," it was chaired by the Secretary of War and included the Secretary's assistant George L. Harrison, James F. Byrnes (Truman's personal representative), Under Secretary Ralph A. Bard, Assistant Secretary of State William L. Clayton, and scientists Bush, Conant, and Karl T. Compton.

James Conant's reaction to receiving an invitation to serve on the Interim Committee illustrates the scientist's concern that it was essential for the scientific task force at work on the bomb to be fully represented. Knowing the dissenting opinion of Szilard, Franck and others, Conant urged that more scientists be brought into the framework of discussion and that their views be communicated to the President. A Scientific Panel was appointed, including Compton, Fermi, Lawrence, and Oppenheimer. Scientists, it seemed, were to be at the right hand of the Secretary of War as he pondered the use of the bomb and the postwar consequences. Scientists were to give advice on the weapon which was still in development but of which they felt so sure that they were very disturbed over its postwar control. Although President Truman would make the ultimate decision, Stimson was the man in the driver's seat and he was the man to influence. Time was running short as the timetable of the bomb project and that of the war raced each other to a conclusion.

Defense leaders, statesmen, and scientists met in the first of a series of conferences. The forty-one-year-old Oppenheimer looked ten years younger despite the crushing strain of work at Los Alamos and was listened to with respect born of wonder for the twentieth-century alchemy being brewed in his laboratory. Lawrence, the inventor of the cyclotron, was his usual dynamic self, and Fermi was as deferential as might be expected at his first high-level session in Washington since his meeting with naval authorities six years earlier. The Compton brothers were impressive; their striking appearances gave them an air of authority. Of all the scientists, Arthur Compton bore the responsibility for representing the dissident views of his Metallurgical Laboratory malcontents. General Groves was fuming over what he interpreted as an effort to go over his head when, some weeks earlier, Szilard had visited Byrnes. Groves was outranked by General George C. Marshall, who was present.

During the morning discussion of S-1, Ernest Lawrence is reported to have made the suggestion that there be a demonstration of the weapon in such a way as to impress the Japanese without excessive loss of life. At lunch the idea of a demonstration of the bomb's power came up and many objections were raised. It was agreed that the demonstration might not be impressive and then the United States would have tipped its hand and prejudiced the use of the bomb at a time when the Japanese defense would be forewarned. They could concentrate interceptory fire on the attacking bombers, or evacuate cities, or move in American prisoners of war. Then, too, the S-1 might not work; either it might fail to detonate properly, due to fusing troubles, or it might be a low-yield and unimpressive bomb. Discussion focused on the question of what warning might be given to the Japanese in advance of the atomic attack; Stimson concluded that *no warning could be given.*

Secretary Stimson's words then described the Committee's recommendations:

> On June 1, after its discussions with the Scientific Panel, the Interim Committee unanimously adopted the following recommendations:
> (1) The bomb should be used against Japan as soon as possible.
> (2) It should be used on a dual target—that is, a military installation or war plant surrounded by or adjacent to houses and other buildings most susceptible to damage, and
> (3) It should be used without prior warning.

The above quotation is from Stimson's article "The Decision to Use the Atomic Bomb" published in *Harper's Magazine*. Mr. Stimson did not include in this article a highly significant observation—that he had already made up his mind on the use of the bomb, as of May 28, 1945. The following quotation, derived from a review of Stimson's *Memoirs,* was published in 1962 by the Atomic Energy Commission: "For him, the issue was not whether to use the new weapon. Rather, it was how to end the war against Japan and safeguard the true interests of the United States throughout the world. The prospect of a long, bloody war in the Far East weighed heavily upon him. If the atomic lightning could shorten it, he would not hesitate to hurl the bolt."

It would seem that the Secretary had made up his mind about the use of the weapon prior to meeting with the scientists. Furthermore, the Scientific Panel had no opportunity to reflect and prepare its own report; the Committee seconded Stimson. The latter could be a very single-minded individual, as his hunting companions had found when on the track of bear.

In any event, the Scientific Panel was scarcely in a position to contend with defense officials on military matters. To be sure, Oppenheimer and the other scientists knew what the A-bomb would do, but they were, with few exceptions, unschooled in details of how the war was going in the Pacific. In order for the scientists to render an intelligent opinion on the use of the bomb against Japan and its probable impact, they needed to know the condition of the beleaguered island empire and the specifics of U.S. war plans for invasion and conquest. As Oppenheimer admitted afterward: "We didn't know beans about the military situation. We didn't know whether they [the Japanese] could be caused to surrender by other means or whether invasion was really inevitable."

At the first meeting of the Interim Committee, the Scientific Panel was asked to prepare a statement of the kind of organization that scientists believed should be set up for the postwar development of atomic energy. Arthur Compton, still troubled by his dissenters in Chicago, asked if these scientists could be informed of the discussions at the Interim Committee meeting. It was agreed that they could be told that Stimson chaired the committee, but that its membership would not be disclosed. When Compton returned to Chicago he promptly summoned leading scientists to a conference and explained that the Scientific Panel would be reporting very soon to the Interim Committee. He solicited the views of the scientists and organized a number of committees to proceed in the analysis of varied aspects of organization, production, education, security, social, and political implications. James Franck was appointed to head discussion of the latter area. One biologist, James J. Nickson, joined the Franck group, which was comprised of physicists and chemists—Leo Szilard, Donald J. Hughes, Eugene Rabinowitch, Joyce Stearns, and Glenn T. Seaborg.

Although historians may date the inception of the Franck Committee as June 2, 1945, it was already in existence as a loosely organized discussion group at the Metallurgical Laboratory and dated back to the previous summer. Thus when the seven Chicago scientists put their heads together to ponder the assignment for the Scientific Panel, they had the advantage of some months of thinking. Their effort to assemble a report in a week's time must therefore be viewed as something far more than a hurried look at the social and political implications of atomic energy. The final draft of the report was finished on June 11, 1945, and the next day

Franck and Compton attempted to present it to Stimson, but they had to be content with leaving a copy at the Secretary's office.

The Franck Report represented a crisis of conscience for the seven scientists at Chicago; their report focused on warning against the use of the bomb against Japan. Although it is clear that these men were appalled by the moral aspect of indiscriminate mass destruction of a civilian population, they refrained from moralizing in their study. Nor did they mourn the malicious debut of atomic energy as a weapon of destruction rather than as a force for construction. The scientists were not in a position to tangle with the Secretary of War on matters of intelligence about the status of Japan's will to resist and they had only the faintest inkling of U.S. war plans for the next year. They appreciated the need to bring the war in the Pacific to a close without a costly invasion of Japan. It is against this background that the recommendations of the Franck Committee must be viewed.

"All of us, familiar with the present state of nucleonics, live with the vision before our eyes of sudden destruction visited upon our own country," a preamble to the report read, "of a Pearl Harbor disaster magnified a thousand-fold and repeated in every one of our major cities." Thus attention was called to the fact that if we used the bomb first, our turn would come. There was a lengthy discussion of technical aspects of weapon development by other nations, stipulating that it might "take other nations three or four years to overcome our present headstart, and eight to ten years to draw even with us even if we should continue to do intensive work in this field." (General Groves told the Interim Committee it would take twenty years for another country to get the A-bomb.) Very clearly the scientists were saying that the decision to use the bomb should be treated as a critical political determination, set far apart from a purely military decision. The Franck Report acknowledged that the use of the A-bomb without warning had certain military advantages, such as the saving of human life, if the war should end as a result, but it pointed out that there was a precedent for nonuse of potent weapons, namely, poison gas. However, it

argued that military advantages might be "outweighed by the ensuing loss of confidence and by a wave of horror and repulsion
sweeping over the rest of the world and perhaps even dividing
public opinion at home." It recommended:

From this point of view, a demonstration of the new weapon might
best be made, before the eyes of representatives of all the United
Nations, on the desert or a barren island. The best possible atmosphere
for the achievement of an international agreement could be achieved
if America could say to the world, "You see what sort of weapon we
had but did not use. We are ready to renounce its use in the future if
other nations join us in this renunciation and agree to the establishment
of an efficient international control."

After such a demonstration the weapon might perhaps be used
against Japan if the sanction of the United Nations (and of public
opinion at home) were obtained, perhaps, after a preliminary ultimatum
to Japan to surrender or at least to evacuate certain regions as an alternative to total destruction. This may sound fantastic, but in nuclear weapons we have something entirely new in order of magnitude of destructive power, and if we want to capitalize fully on the advantage their
possession gives us, we must use new and imaginative methods.

The atomic scientists at Chicago had spoken with a sense of urgency
because—to use their own words—"we found ourselves, by the
force of events, during the last five years, in the position of a small
group of citizens cognizant of a grave danger for the safety of this
country as well as for the future of all the other nations, of which
the rest of mankind is unaware."

The Franck Report was referred to the Scientific Panel for com-
ment, but the four scientists could not agree that a purely technical
test of the weapon would be sufficiently impressive to the Japanese.
On June 21, the Interim Committee met in executive session, but
the Secretary of War was not present; the Committee reaffirmed
the recommendations made three weeks earlier and the die was cast.
It would be direct military use of S-1, the targets for which General
Groves had given final approval only a week before. The date of
November 1, 1945, had already been set for Operation *Olympic,*
the assault upon Kyushu, and the Joint Chiefs of Staff were pro-

ceeding on the assumption that Japan would be reduced to surrender by conventional means.

The Chicago scientists had failed in their appeal to the Secretary
of War, but the formalization of views by the Franck Report stimulated discussion within the Metallurgical Laboratory. Furthermore,
since it was not entirely clear to the scientists at Chicago what the
Scientific Panel was supposed to do or how the Interim Committee
would function (they did not even know who was on the Committee) some scientists like Szilard were uneasy. Had Szilard
known that the Committee had already filed its conclusion on June
1, he would have been up in arms, but he had no way of learning
this surprising fact. Nonetheless, he did not suddenly cease his
"meddling" when he learned that the Scientific Panel had rejected
the major recommendation of the Franck Report, namely, the
technical demonstration of the bomb. Instead, the wily Szilard set
about finding some way to bypass the Pentagon and go directly to
the White House. Because of his previous experience he knew that
a letter-to-the-President technique would not work; he needed a
new approach and he found it in the form of a petition. Szilard's
resort to an old form of democratic procedure was to produce
consternation in General Groves's office. Further security pre-
cautions had been enforced within S-1 during June and this was
the tip-off to many scientists that the day of the first A-test was
drawing near. To my knowledge only two people, Arthur Compton
and myself, were then allowed to commute between Chicago and
Los Alamos. All other traffic from Chicago was strictly forbidden;
this, too, was a dead giveaway to knowledgeable scientists that a
critical juncture in atomic events was being approached. Szilard
knew the production schedules for Hanford and he could project
quite easily when there would be enough bomb material for as-
sembling a weapon. This made Szilard even more determined to
air his views in Washington before the momentum of events made
counteraction impossible.

During the first two weeks in July, Szilard circulated a paper
titled "A Petition to the President of the United States" and col-
lected a total of sixty-nine signatures of qualified scientists. He did

not "load" his petition by asking technicians, mechanics, or secretaries to sign, because these people were not cleared to receive information of the type Szilard discussed. The petition stressed the moral responsibility involved in use of the bomb which would open "the door to an era of devastation on an unimaginable scale" and make it difficult for the United States to line up support among other nations for international control of the atom. It called for making public terms of surrender for Japan; should Japan refuse the terms, the President should still take full account of the moral responsibility for his decision to use the new weapon.

Arthur Compton has given us an account of these times in his book *The Atomic Quest*. He relates that Szilard's petition inspired counterpetitions by scientists who felt that the bomb should be used promptly to avert further loss of American lives in the war. I personally was surprised to read this because I was on the spot at the time and never saw any counterpetition or heard of any. But then this whole section of Compton's book has a curious ring which appears to me to be a rationalization of the use of the bomb. In any event, Szilard's petitioning agitated General Groves to the point where he asked Compton to have a poll taken at Chicago. Dr. Farrington Daniels had just been made director of the Metallurgical Laboratory and I had been appointed assistant to him. Accordingly a voluntary and informal poll was conducted at the Chicago laboratory on July 12, 1945, four days before the first A-bomb was tested in New Mexico (only two scientists there were officially aware of the date of this impending test). One hundred and fifty scientists or well over half of the professional staff voted in secret on the following five choices for the use of the bomb. Numbers given in parentheses after each option represent first the number of scientists voting for that choice and the percentage of the total for this figure:

QUESTION: *Which of the following five procedures comes closest to your choice as to the way in which any new weapons we may develop should be used in the Japanese war?*

    1. Use them in the manner that is from the military point of view most effective in bringing about prompt Japanese surrender at

minimum human cost to our armed forces. (*23 votes or 15 per cent*)

2. Give a military demonstration in Japan to be followed by renewed opportunity for surrender before full use of the weapon is employed. (*69 votes or 46 per cent*)

3. Give an experimental demonstration in this country, with representatives of Japan present; followed by a new opportunity for surrender before full use of the weapon is employed. (*39 votes or 26 per cent*)

4. Withhold military use of the weapons, but make public experimental demonstration of their effectiveness. (*16 votes or 11 per cent*)

5. Maintain as secret as possible all developments of our new weapons and refrain from using them in this war. (*3 votes or 2 per cent*)

The results were turned over to Compton the next day and then forwarded to Washington on July 24. Compton recalls that he was asked for his personal opinion and gave it: "My vote is with the majority. It seems to me that as the war stands the bomb should be used, but no more drastically than needed to bring surrender."

How did the war stand in July when the first A-bomb was detonated at Alamogordo, New Mexico? The scientists who had been polled at Chicago knew about as much as they read in the pages of the Chicago *Tribune*. Arthur Compton's knowledge must have been better, but there is no record that he was briefed on official developments at the Pentagon. Thus if the question about the use of the bomb is keyed to military necessity, one needed to know the condition of Japan as well as U.S. war plans. If Japan were tottering on the brink of defeat, then one could argue (*a*) that a sensational display of nuclear might would suffice to push it over, or (*b*) that if the situation were so desperate, continued conventional force would be sufficient.

Secretary Stimson's record reveals the nature of U.S. war plans:

The strategic plans of our armed forces for the defeat of Japan, as they stood in July, had been prepared without reliance upon the atomic bomb. We were planning an intensified sea and air blockade, and greatly intensified strategic air bombing, through the summer and early fall, to be followed on November 1 by an invasion of the main island of Kyushu. This would be followed in turn by an invasion of the main island of Honshu in the spring of 1946. The total U.S. military and naval force involved in this grand design was of the order of 5,000,000 men; if all those indirectly concerned are included, it was larger still. We estimated that if we should be forced to carry this plan to its conclusion, the major fighting would not end until the latter part of 1946, at the earliest. I was informed that such operations might be expected to cost over a million casualties to American forces alone. Additional large losses might be expected among our allies and, of course, if our campaign were successful and if we could judge by previous experience, enemy casualties would be much larger than our own.

It seems to me unnecessary to describe further the scientists' endeavors to affect a decision on the use of the bomb. With such war plans in existence, the Secretary of War who approved them and the President who received them would not take seriously the arguments raised by the scientists. As the AEC history records: "Nothing could have seemed more irrelevant to Stimson and Harrison on August 1 than further expositions of scientific opinion."

Had the scientists at Chicago been confronted with the war projections detailed above by Stimson, they might well have voted overwhelmingly for direct military use of the bomb. But had they also been given access to photointelligence about the condition of Japan, they would have backed away from such precipitous conclusions and reconsidered the entire matter. Neither the scientists in Chicago nor the illustrious Scientific Panel knew how badly our armed might had mauled Japan. As Admiral Ernest J. King records in his recollections:

The President in giving his approval for these [atomic] attacks appeared to believe that many thousands of American troops would be killed in invading Japan, and in this he was entirely correct; but King [he refers to himself in the third person throughout his book] felt, as he pointed out many times that the dilemma was an unnecessary one, for had we been willing to wait, the effective naval blockade would, in the course of time have starved the Japanese into submission through lack of oil, rice, medicines, and other essential materials. The Army, however, with its underestimation of sea power, had insisted upon a direct invasion and an occupational conquest of Japan proper.

Admiral King could have added, had he wished to credit the effects of the air attack on Japan, that low level B-29 raids on Japan's major cities had produced saturation effects, meaning that no more damage could be inflicted upon certain target areas. Aerial reconnaissance showed almost two million buildings destroyed in sixty-six of Japan's largest cities. To continue on in this vein is to turn back the pages of history in a wistful or "what might have been" fashion. As President, Harry S Truman comments on the advice he received from the Interim Committee, brought to him on June 1 by Secretary Stimson: "It was their recommendation that the bomb be used against the enemy as soon as it could be done. They recommended further that it should be used without specific warning and against a target that would clearly show its devastating strength." Truman's *Memoirs* gives no hint that he received any counsel from the scientists after June 1, 1945 (which is when they *began* their discussions for the Interim Committee), or that he ever saw the Szilard petition. "The final decision of where and when to use the atomic bomb was up to me," Truman writes, and, "I regarded the bomb as a military weapon and never had any doubt that it should be used."

The scientists who had played multiple roles as initiators, provocateurs, and developers of the new weapon found themselves powerless to influence its military application. Their secret dissent during the last few months of the war was futile with respect to altering the decision on the bomb, but it laid the basis for their active participation in a great debate on the atomic issue following Hiroshima and Nagasaki. Without the Chicago rebellion and its repercussions, one might be justified in deploring a lack of social responsibility among the scientists. It is to their credit that some of them undertook a secret dialogue despite the odds and the pressures mounted against them.

Why then did the War Department bother to consult the scientists if their counsel was to be *post facto?* Here the record is blurred and a *post mortem* examination is rendered difficult by the fact that official records of the time have not been declassified. Furthermore, much that could be significant is hidden in cortical crevices beyond recall. But a therapy motive may be ascribed to those in charge of the S-1 work: if the scientists within the project had not been allowed some internal vent for their dissent, they might have built up pressure and blown S-1 security sky-high. General Groves was haunted by the possibility that news of the A-bomb might leak out and rob the United States forces of the element of surprise in the use of the weapon. "To achieve surprise," wrote General Groves in *Now It Can Be Told,* "was one of the reasons we tried so hard to maintain our security." General Groves was also deeply worried, as he confided to an associate after the war, that Congress might learn about the project and start an investigation of S-1. "Our work was extremely costly," he wrote, "both in money and in its interference with the rest of the war effort. As time went on, as we poured more and more money and effort into the project, the government became increasingly committed to the ultimate use of the bomb, and while it has often been said that we undertook development of this terrible weapon so that Hitler would not get it first, the fact remains that the original decision to make the project an all-out effort was based upon using it to end the war."

General Groves devotes very few paragraphs in his book *Now It Can Be Told* to the decision on the use of the bomb. His only reference to the Chicago dissenters is contained in three sentences: "A little later some of the scientists began to express doubts about the desirability of using the bomb against Japan. A number of these men had come to the United States to escape racial persecution under the Hitler regime. To them, Hitler was the supreme enemy and, once he had been destroyed, they apparently found themselves unable to generate the same degree of enthusiasm for destroying Japan's military power." Japan posed no threat as a competitor in the race to get the A-bomb, and the scientists' frame of reference for developing the bomb was no longer the same.

Yet when General Groves states that "the government became

increasingly committed to the ultimate use of the bomb" the reader is left with many questions unanswered. The S-1 project was ultra-secret and relatively few men in government know about the bomb —how then did they "commit" themselves to the use of the bomb? Were they afraid that if the bomb were not used in a dramatic fashion that there would be recrimination against project officials? Or were officials worried that premature publicity on the bomb might lead to a more general revolt of the scientists and perhaps even a public outcry against the weapon? Or did the decision-makers fear that Hiroshima might produce a backlash of criticism and charges of immorality? In such an event, it would be useful to have on hand a record of consultation with some of the nation's top scientists.

The muffled words of counsel, which a small group of scientists uttered, relayed through the formality of the Franck Report to a then anonymous Interim Committee, constituted an imperfect and unsuccessful dialogue. (To this day the original Franck Report has not been released by the Pentagon.) A few scientists were anguished by what playwright Arthur Miller called a "complicity with murder," but more were deeply worried about the control of the new force in the postwar period. A power too tempting to be spurned by the nation's policy-makers was used at Hiroshima, but it would not be buried there.

The nuclear scientists realized more than anyone else that the bombs dropped at Hiroshima and Nagasaki were not the end of the matter. Control of nuclear research and of the use of nuclear power was at stake. The atomic experts had great hopes for putting the atom to the service of mankind, especially in providing the planet with a new substitute flameless fuel that would replace coal. They feared the further use of modern power in war could destroy civilization.

In the days after the first A-bombs, much of their warnings of the future seemed idealistic and long term; people tired of bloodshed were not anxious to think about the possibility of a nuclear holocaust. The single topic which served both to focus the scientists' efforts and to excite them to the need for group action was the issue of civilian versus military control of atomic energy.

The nuclear scientist was little skilled in the art of expressing himself in terms that the public could understand. His was a language that fell strangely upon the layman's ears; and the things of which he spoke were like those of another planet. His talk of neutrons, nuclei and atoms, of chain reactions and nuclear radiation, and of a hundred other things left the ordinary citizen bewildered. What, in fact, did these scientists want from him? How could the average person respond to the dialogue which arose after Hiroshima?

The scientists were not sure what they expected from the public; their pent-up vocal energies were largely directed to education and enlightenment and they did not perceive that the public needed to be confronted with an issue which had significance to it and upon which it could take action. The issue of international control of atomic energy was too diffuse for the public to grasp; it was not something which was within their power to act upon. The scientists' concern over the military control of atomic energy, on the other hand, intrigued the public because it involved controversy and made news, but again the issue did not solidify in the public mind. Something had to have an emotional appeal and jolt the public's sensibility before it would become aroused.

The gap between science and the public was already large before the war, but events in the war years so much accelerated the pace of science and technology that it became vastly greater in 1945. It was to fill this gulf that scientists plunged into their campaign of public enlightenment. Though this was not a task for which many of the atomic scientists were well qualified, they made a valiant effort to speak to the laymen. Looking back to these early days, it is hard to make a judgment of how well they succeeded in educating them. Education is a slow process at best and the necessity for swift action on atomic legislation forced the scientists to whip up support quickly. They found, as all experts on communication have discovered, that it is easier to appeal to emotion than to intellect. It was the strongly emotional issue of military versus civilian control of atomic energy—the visualization of a conspiring adversary in uniform—that created rapport for the scientists.

THE MERGING
OF
5 # THE CULTS

When the scientists hit upon the theme of the danger of military control of the atom, they were finally operating on the public's sensitive wave length. Now one could picture a plot to mastermind the custody of atomic energy. The dramatic potential of this issue received a boost in November, 1945, when the news was flashed from Tokyo that three university cyclotrons had been confiscated by U.S. authorities, and scientific apparatus had been consigned to the Pacific Ocean. Secretary of War Robert Patterson manfully took responsibility for the act and did not even reveal that it was General Groves who gave the order. Scientists reacted to this news as though the cyclotrons had been their own, and the public discerned a sinister move afoot to shackle U.S. science. This windfall did much to strengthen the scientists' case for a civilian Atomic Energy Commission.

The situation at the end of the war was very confused; a multitude of problems had to be dealt with in the Pentagon and atomic energy was only one of these. Furthermore, the issues involved in this single field were both complex and controversial. On the problem of what to do about Russia there were many views among officials like Stimson, Secretary of the Navy James Forrestal, Secretary of State James Byrnes and Commerce Secretary Henry Wallace. The latter took the view that cooperation in atomic energy should be extended to Russia, whereas Forrestal and Byrnes took a hard line against such a policy. Stimson, exhausted by the war years, hoped that some negotiation with Russia might be possible. In this atmosphere the War Department drafted what became known as the Royall-Marbury bill (General Kenneth C. Royall had been named to succeed Robert P. Patterson as Undersecretary of War, and William L. Marbury was a legal counsel in the Pentagon).

The scientists at Chicago, hardy rebels that they were, learned that something was afoot; although not consulted, they managed to find out about the War Department's bill. The news which they received, together with reports that they heard about Byrnes's attitude toward international control, aroused them to action. There was at the level of the working scientists a resentment of science administrators like Bush and Conant who, they felt, were too far removed from research and the atmosphere of the laboratory to be in a position to draft or to help prepare legislation for a Commission to take over the affairs of the Manhattan Project. In part, this lack of confidence derived from a feeling that the scientists had been "sold out" by the Scientific Panel and the scientists on the Interim Committee. While this feeling was not general within the groups of scientists at the atomic sites, it was shared by a number at Chicago. Some of them were gathered together at the Institute for Nuclear Studies at the University of Chicago. Perturbed by the threat of continued army control over atomic research, Samuel K. Allison, who was the man whose words timed the first detonation of the A-bomb at Alamogordo, made a plea for unfettered research saying that if this was not possible then "scientists should study the color of butterfly wings." Allison's colorful language, together with Enrico Fermi's and Harold Urey's admonitions, got wide press attention. General Groves took a flying trip to the Midway campus to scold the scientists about their criticism of a bill that they had not yet seen, but the fat was in the fire. Now the big guns of physics, the Ureys, Szilards, Francks, and the older men, were reinforced by growing numbers of younger scientists of whom the public had heard nothing.

One of the new-generation physicists who had matured within

the Manhattan Project was Dr. John Simpson, a short, squarish-built bachelor not yet thirty, who was an expert in electronic circuitry. Mild in manner and deliberate in speech, Dr. Simpson did not look the part of a Chicago rebel, but he was a moving force in the effort which scientists made to block military domination of atomic research. He had been a conscientious member of the Committee on Social and Political Implications which grew out of the Franck-Szilard conferences at Chicago earlier that summer. In September, 1945, he decided to devote full time to the fight for civilian control. As he later expressed it: "Our efforts were directed towards the preparation of speeches, newspaper articles, magazine articles, radio talks and conferences with community leaders. Reaching the public was a new experience for us." The atomic scientists were quick to appreciate that they needed some organization and means for keeping in touch with one another. Many had left their wartime posts to return to universities and there was a grave danger that they would dissipate their efforts unless some harmony could be created among them. On September 13 a group consisting largely of the Chicago rebels formed an organization called the Atomic Scientists of Chicago with the avowed purpose to:

1. Explore, clarify and consolidate the opinion of scientists on the problems of the role and responsibility of science particularly as far as the implications of atomic power are concerned.

2. Present this opinion before the national administration and to influence the decisions which this country will have to make in the field of atomic power research and applications and the international problems resulting from it.

3. Educate public opinion to the full understanding of the scientific, technological and political implications of the new scientific development, particularly those resulting from atomic power.

The Chicago movement was paralleled by the rise of similar protest-action groups in Los Alamos, New York, and Oak Ridge. The spread of the revolt cannot be entirely ascribed to a desire to head off the Pentagon in its power play; it was also a reaction to the confusion which had been mushrooming in the public press.

As John Simpson expressed it: "Weird and dangerous conclusions were being formed by citizens throughout the country. A new era had exploded into existence before the citizens of our nation and the world, and its implications might well stagger the imagination."

Was Simpson's assertion really true? Presumably the Pentagon might have stepped in to dispel the confusion, but this would have meant relegating the job to General Groves or to the Interim Committee. But if General Groves had moved more into the public sector he would have risked exposing the War Department's attitude on postwar control of the atom and further antagonizing the scientists. Moreover, General Groves was cordially disliked by a very influential group of senior army officers in the Pentagon who resented his spectacular rise to prominence and his high-handed methods of operation. As for the Interim Committee, it was a group that met infrequently and its scientist members were inundated with a postwar deluge of unfinished business and plans for the future. As the scientist groups busied themselves with organizing chores they were only dimly aware of the Pentagon's draft of a bill for an Atomic Commission. Dr. Vannevar Bush was consulted on the draft and he offered many objections, but he was himself not fully in the confidence of the scientists at the working level. It is conceivable that Dr. Bush could have personally ameliorated the situation a great deal if he had spoken out to the scientists. However, his manner was autocratic and his views were often those of the engineer and the administrator, rather than those of the scientist and researcher. Grown accustomed to power, Dr. Bush was more used to operating in lofty policy circles than in the hurly-burly of the public arena. Suffice it to say that he did not inspire confidence among the protest groups of scientists who organized in the first few months after the end of World War II.

But suddenly, on October 9, 1945, an issue crystallized which was to excite the scientists and to focus their efforts. On that day the Military Affairs Committee of the House of Representatives reported out a bill for the military control of atomic energy. This legislation, introduced by Representative Andrew J. May (Ky.)

and Senator Edwin Johnson (Colo.), was given a "quickie" one-day hearing. H.R. 4280 was "An Act for the Development and Control of Atomic Energy" before the Committee on Military Affairs. The bill called for a nine-member commission to serve for nine years with broad and sweeping powers which could, its critics felt, restrict all atomic research to government agencies, immunize the commission from public review of atomic policy, exclude private enterprise in nuclear power, bottle up atomic information, and impose severe security restrictions on scientists. Military officers would not be excluded from appointment to the nine-member commission. It was a power play designed to steam roller the War Department's bill through the Congress. To be sure, there was some reason for the Pentagon to demand prompt action from the legislators; the fate of the wartime atomic project was in limbo until the Congress passed legislation deciding it. On Capitol Hill the atom was a puzzler since it did not really belong to any established committee although a number had an interest in it. There was much jockeying back and forth as various Congressmen introduced bills of their own to stake a claim on the atom. Unless action was forthcoming soon a hopeless stalemate would result from a logjam of conflicting bills.

General Royall, principal architect of the War Department's bill, was the lead-off witness before the Military Affairs Committee. In his opening statement he placed the authority of the Interim Committee and the Scientific Panel squarely behind the proposed legislation. No questions were asked of the first witness and General Groves took the witness seat. His testimony made it abundantly evident that the bill was to his liking. Dr. Vannevar Bush followed Groves and gave his endorsement to the bill as did his colleague Dr. Conant, who urged prompt congressional action. The newly appointed Secretary of War Robert P. Patterson was the final witness and he naturally gave it wholehearted support. Representative May banged his gavel and the hearing was over. The one-day hearing aroused the atomic scientists who interpreted it as a railroading through of a bill designed to give control of atomic energy to the military. Scientists at Los Alamos, Oak Ridge, New York, and

Chicago were hastily rounded up to apply pressure to force the May-Johnson bill to be reopened for hearings.

Some of the scientists felt that they had either been betrayed or outmaneuvered. Others believed that Oppenheimer and Fermi, who were not in the mainstream of Washington affairs, had been hoodwinked on the bill. Szilard was incensed by the ramrod tactics of the May committee and he marshaled support to block action on the bill. Meanwhile, the Interim Committee scientists began to have second thoughts about their approval of the May-Johnson bill. Not only had they lent the weight of their prestige to the legislation, they had assured their colleagues in laboratories and universities that the bill was not prejudicial to their interests and had cautioned them against interfering with its passage. In retrospect it would appear that men like Oppenheimer and Fermi were not up to tilting with Pentagon lawyers in the dull game of bill drafting. One had to read the draft legislation very carefully to perceive its meaning and probable interpretation; Fermi was interested in scientific experiments, not lawyer's phrases, and Oppenheimer was probably insufficiently informed on Pentagon politics.

The crisis over the May-Johnson bill produced a split among the scientists because Oppenheimer and the Scientific Panel endorsed the bill. But apart from this top-level fissure, the concentration of effort on a single objective fused together groups of scientists from various laboratories and gave them a new exhilarating sense of unity.

Scientists trooped to Washington to form the strangest, most ill-equipped lobby that the city had ever seen. The newly turned-out lobbyists were innocent in the ways of politics and naïve in their understanding of legislative matters. They had only fragmentary organization and meager personal funds to finance their operations. But counterbalancing these drawbacks, they had a common cause to which they could dedicate their zeal. Furthermore, they soon found friends in many walks of life and they discovered that Washington reporters were ready to listen to them and their editors were willing to play up their stories. In short, they discovered that they had voices which commanded some attention. Their outcries over the stringent secrecy provisions of the May-Johnson bill were all in one pitch attuned to the need for science to remain free. They had other grievances to air and they stirred up enough furor to force Congressman May to reopen the hearings.

On October 18 when the hearings resumed Dr. Szilard was the first witness. It was his first appearance before a congressional committee and he met with a rather hostile reception. Some members of the committee, it was rumored, had been provided with information designed to discomfit him. Whatever the truth of this report, the committee had barbed questions to shoot at Szilard in a thinly veiled move to harass him. A ranking Texan, R. Ewing Thomason, was keenly interested in Szilard's patent troubles with the government (the scientist had about eight inventions to his credit but he refused to sign patent papers until he could obtain the advice of a patent attorney—a maneuver which would require clearing an "outsider," a procedure Groves refused to approve). Despite the congressional crossfire, Szilard voiced strong objections to passage of the bill. His somewhat arrogant manner reminded one of a professor-to-student relationship and was not appreciated by the Congressmen; nor did they become endeared to his discursive replies, accented as they were with a Hungarian lilt. As he stepped down from testifying, one member of the committee was overheard to say: "It's a good thing that General Groves invented the A-bomb."

Arthur Compton, the next witness, was a welcome relief to the committee. His dynamic appearance, not unlike that of a very successful American businessman, and his measured words inspired confidence, as did his record of appointment to many government advisory bodies. But Compton was the only one of the four scientists on the Interim Committee's Panel who had withheld judgment on the War Department's bill. Now he proceeded to raise objections to it, thus immensely weakening the support which it had enjoyed when Bush and Conant had backed it. Dr. Oppenheimer followed Compton's testimony and threw his weight with that of Bush and Conant. Next to be called before the committee was

Harold C. Urey, Nobel prize-winner and most widely quoted of all atomic scientists, but he had left the hearing to confer in Senator Glen Taylor's office. Representative May was scarcely anxious to call in Dr. Urey, but he allowed his statement to be placed in the record.

Urey's criticism of the May-Johnson bill was both the most destructive and yet the most constructive of any witness. He blasted the bill, finding it hopeless to amend, and gave the advice that: "The whole bill should be rewritten by other men who have an entirely different point of view about the whole program." He scored the bill's excessive secrecy provisions as "almost fantastic" and asserted that its military emphasis "will hamper all attempts to secure international control of atomic bombs." But at the same time he gave a reasoned critique of the administrative organization proposed for the new Commission and suggested many changes which in fact were later written into law.

The scientists may have overreacted in jumping in feet first to stomp on the May-Johnson bill so vehemently, but they most certainly killed the War Department's bill. A rift was opened between the scientists and the Pentagon, and relationships between top level scientists and their lower level associates were strained or even ruptured. Emboldened by their successful sally on Capitol Hill, the atomic scientists set about regrouping their forces and girding themselves for new battles.

One thing that the scientists learned from their forays into public affairs was that they had to coordinate their efforts. This meant organization and effective communication between scientists. Fortunately, the national publicity attending the May-Johnson bill ruckus alerted scientists all over the country and made them anxious to join forces. Young men like Harrison Brown and Spofford English of Oak Ridge, Willie Higinbotham and David Hill of Los Alamos joined with the Chicago group which was spearheaded by Eugene Rabinowitch, H. H. Goldsmith, and John Simpson. Six groups of these scientists representing various atomic sites got together on October 31, 1945, and founded the Federation of Atomic Scientists (today known as the Federation of American Scientists or simply as F.A.S.). The newly formed Federation shrewdly limited itself to scientist members and avoided merging with nonscientist organizations where it might lose its identity.

The new organization of atomic scientists was no model of efficiency or of smooth operation. But what it lacked in these respects it more than made up for in sheer zeal and activity. A National Committee on Atomic Information was formed both to keep members informed as to F.A.S. activities and also to spread atomic enlightenment to the public. Scientists like Willie Higinbotham were always available to speak before church or community groups or to rush over to Capitol Hill and brief Congressmen or staff members on atomic issues. It was, all in all, a shoestring operation in which the participants paid their own way, stayed with friends or at cheap hotels in Washington, and often had their meals at cocktail parties. Atomic scientists had acquired sufficient status to be sought after by Washington hostesses.

Older men like Eugene Rabinowitch knew that scientists were going to have a long pull in their struggle to educate the public and to influence national policy. Some method of exchanging and airing views would be needed to be effective over the years. The Russian-born Rabinowitch, a chemist at the University of Illinois, was adept at writing—much more so than at speaking—and it was natural for him to think in terms of a publication. He and Hy Goldsmith founded the *Bulletin of the Atomic Scientists*. The first edition came out on December 10, 1945 (its original name included the words "of Chicago" after "Scientists," but this qualification was dropped early the next year), as a folded two-sheet publication. The modest little biweekly soon turned into an impressive monthly magazine with a board of sponsors that included the most famous names in American science. Dr. Goldsmith was soon to die in a swimming accident, but Rabinowitch kept a steady hand on the magazine throughout its history. Its pages were to feature the most informed debate on atomic issues and it must be ranked as a profoundly influential journal of our times.

It is well to recall that the society of scientists which lobbied so hard for an Atomic Energy Act did not represent the whole of the scientific community. Moreover, the controversy which flared over the provisions of the May-Johnson bill showed that there was no unanimous agreement among scientists. It made clear that there was no consensus in the scientific community. The momentum of the movement doubled the number of scientists taking an active interest in public affairs, as represented by membership in the Federation of American Scientists. No poll was ever taken to determine how the scientists would have voted on their support or disavowal of the atomic legislation, but the loose network of scientist groups that sprang up in the aftermath of Hiroshima encompassed over a thousand scientists in the fall of 1945 and grew to double this number within a year. Scientists were streaming away from the wartime posts and they had not yet established themselves in a pattern of postwar research.

Many, like young John Simpson and Higinbotham, were willing to take time out and work in the public interest. "It is important to remember," reflected Simpson in 1947, "that the scientists had no axes to grind. In fact, many of the things we proposed could in no way be construed as benefiting the scientists. We did everything possible to show no political bias as a group." The nonpolitical orientation and altruistic attitude of the scientists was an innovation in a Washington that looked upon lobbyists as scalawags and semi-evil characters. Scientists were somehow different from ordinary folk—at least this was the impression of many.

As controversy was kindled about the control of the atom, a young freshman Senator from Connecticut, Brien McMahon, maneuvered to head up a special committee on atomic energy. It required deft political footwork for the Irish newcomer to get his prize, but he was canny enough to sense that the atom was the key to his future and he finally got his wish. Once he won the committee chairmanship (which he did on October 27 after nosing out his rival, Senator Edwin Johnson) he searched for the means of proceeding which would live up to the challenge of the atom.

Unfortunately, his special committee was packed with Senators of strongly conservative hue and he had his job cut out for him if he wished to breathe life into the group. For one thing, the Senators needed to be educated and for another, the committee needed an expert staff.

Through chance acquaintance, McMahon became attracted to the talents of a young New Deal lawyer who worked as head of the Science Division of the Office of War Mobilization. The lawyer, James R. Newman, combined the qualities of a keen legal mind with an appreciation of science that no other lawyer could match. Newman acted as White House adviser on science and atomic energy legislation; in this capacity he came to McMahon's attention, although he had previously met him through a mutual friend, Representative Helen Gahagan Douglas (D. Cal.). With his colleague Byron S. Miller, Newman drafted an Atomic Energy Act for Senator McMahon; it was sponsored in the House by Congresswoman Douglas. The new bill gave the United States government a total monopoly on sources of atomic energy and in Newman's own words it was "a radical piece of legislation—in some respects as radical and unprecedented as the scientific discovery that occasioned it." He added: "It is, in sober fact, an act without precedent in the legislative history of this or any other country. Never before have men in any state, standing on the threshold of a new technological era, attempted to provide in advance for rational control of the forces to be unleashed."

Senator McMahon became a force to be reckoned with and he proceeded to align himself with the atomic scientists. His statement that atomic energy "is too big a matter to leave in the hands of the generals" drew applause from the scientists and they offered him their wholehearted assistance. He exhorted his colleagues in the Senate to ponder the implications of the nuclear weapon, stressing that: "The bombing of Hiroshima was the greatest event in world history since the birth of Jesus Christ." The freshman Senator confronted very prickly issues in holding hearings on his atomic legislation. The committee would have to consider the momentous issue of international control, civilian versus military dominance, patent policy, government versus private development of nuclear power, freedom of research and atomic secrecy.

On November 27, 1945, his Special Committee on Atomic Energy opened its investigation. General Groves, as a witness, reiterated his contention that it would take twenty years for another country to make A-bombs. In a press interview earlier, he noted that scientists placed the figure as closer to two or four years; he explained: "But they are thinking of science and theory, not of building and operating a plant to produce the bombs. No one but the men who built those plants could have true appreciation of how long it would take any other country to do the job." This was an estimate with which Vannevar Bush agreed and it is worth high-lighting because the time scale assigned to our nearest competitor would bear upon the problem of secrecy and control. Groves was followed by Dr. Harold C. Urey whose testimony, even if reread today, was impressive. He handled questions with aplomb and he was able to give firsthand examples of the evils of compartmentalization and secrecy. For instance, he cited the fact that the Du Pont Company was told not to discuss heavy-water production methods with him. This was fatuous since no scientist knew more about the subject than Urey and he later learned that the method was a standard one well known to him.

Dr. Bush came before the Senate committee after Urey. Impressed by Nazi success with the V-2, the committee wished to know Bush's opinion of the intercontinental ballistic missile about which there was current speculation in the press. Bush replied with all the crossness of a bear disturbed in midwinter: "There has been a great deal said about a 3,000-mile high-angle rocket. In my opinion, such a thing is impossible today and will be impossible for many years." Upon being pressed for elaboration, Bush referred to the 3,000-mile missile and concluded: "I think we can leave that out of our thinking. I wish the American people would leave that out of their thinking."

The star witness to appear before McMahon's hearing was J. Robert Oppenheimer. His manner of speaking was strangely persuasive, a mixture of slang and overhumility combined with a sense of excitement that the weapons expert might tiptoe a bit over the line of security and let drop an atomic secret or two. Oppenheimer emphasized the atomic production of electric power as he testified that "there would be good reasons for putting a [uranium] power plant in the Yangtze Valley," and the Senator from Colorado, Edwin C. Johnson, cut him down with the observation:

If I had the planning of that, if I were a world conqueror and had any plans for taking over the world, the first thing I would do would be to build a great power plant, plutonium power plant, and then I would secretly develop atomic energy for atomic bombs from that power plant.

I am quite surprised in your statement here this morning advocating the building of a uranium power plant in China.

It seems to me that it is the most reckless proposal I have ever heard made by anyone, scientist or politician or anyone else, because all of us know that there is only a thin line . . . between the development of atomic power, through uranium, and the development of atomic bombs.

The Senator's remarks illustrate that McMahon's attempts to educate his committee had borne some fruit and they should have put the scientists on notice that they could not skip through their testimony without challenge. To be sure, the attention paid to most of Oppenheimer's words approached reverence, but the politicians were not about to relinquish their established positions of power and influence. It is to their credit that they debated as exhaustively as they did the problem of international control. So far as secrecy was concerned the notion that "the atomic secret" was a singular and possessible thing was too firmly fixed in their minds to permit extirpation. They relaxed somewhat the penalty for giving away classified data to a maximum of $20,000 fine, or twenty years imprisonment, or both, but they enshrined atomic secrecy through the mechanism of a curious bit of language. The latter took the form of "restricted data"; this was an oddity to insert into the Atomic Energy Act of 1946 because "restricted" formed the lowest rung on a military classification system which then escalated to "confidential," "secret," and "top secret." Thereafter a new classification "Atomic Energy Restricted Data" came into use. According to the elaborate stipulations of the Act (Sec. 10 Control of Information) no individual could be hired by the new Atomic Energy Commission until the FBI had made a full investigation of his character, associations, and loyalty—a lengthy process which became known as a "Q" clearance.

Actually the form in which the bill was finally passed represented a compromise, as most bills do, of many interests. McMahon had developed the issue of civilian versus military control and had personalized this in a biting attack upon General Groves. Scientists were quick to aim their fire at this target and the McMahon-Gahagan bill might have had smoother sailing had it not been for an unforeseen crisis. In mid-February, 1946, the Canadian spy story broke and implicated scientists in the loss of atomic secrets. Overnight hopes were dashed for early passage of a good atomic energy bill. The War Department took hope that it might be able to resurrect the May-Johnson bill, and General Groves retrieved some of his lost prestige, at least as far as the McMahon committee was concerned.

The battle to regain lost ground was uphill all the way. For a time it even appeared that the Senate would be hopelessly deadlocked on the legislation. Only the most valiant efforts by Senator McMahon and double duty by the skillful committee counsel kept the bill alive. Here Newman was in a strategic position to block War Department maneuvers since he still occupied his post in the White House; he moved from the Capitol to the Executive Office and intercepted War Department overtures to change the McMahon bill. At the same time the Federation of American Scientists labored heroically with other public-spirited groups to apply every possible pressure to the Congress. By now they had acquired some skill in the techniques of lobbying and they used them effectively. To bolster their existing resources they added "Committees for Civilian Control of Atomic Energy" in many locations and a National Committee for Civilian Control was formed. Alfred Friendly, an able reporter for the Washington *Post,* and the respected columnist Marquis Childs threw their support to the scientists. Finally the bill was passed by a voice vote in the U.S. Senate, narrowly avoiding the shoals of treacherous amendments, and it was up to the House to consider the measure. Now the issue was back in Andrew May's hostile Military Affairs Committee where it gave every indication of languishing. As it turned out, May had a vulnerable point; he had had certain dubious relationships with defense contractors and this point of vulnerability was exploited. Reluctantly May gave ground and after complex parliamentary posturing, the bill knife-edged its way through the House. On August 1, 1946, President Truman signed the much contested bill into law and the legislative battle was over.

It would be an exaggeration to say that the scientists had won this battle, for, in fact, they contributed one component to the critical mixture required for passage of the McMahon Act. Even if we assigned them full credit for their role, it would be an overstatement to assert that they had prevailed. The Atomic Energy Act of 1946 was a compromise and it did not represent everything that the scientists desired; that they did not oppose the final version by tacking on extraneous amendments testified to their political sense, for if they had done so, they might have ended up with nothing.

As the fight over military versus civilian control of the atom grew it became apparent that the majority of the vocal scientists bitterly resented General Groves and his ironclad secrecy. Dr. Condon, for example, was not one of Groves's admirers and as scientific adviser to McMahon's special committee, he sent a highly explosive letter to the Pentagon. Condon requested highly classified data on uranium stocks, bomb stockpile, nuclear production rates, and other matters which General Groves had kept ultrasecret. General Groves had no intention of letting these secrets out of his care; he argued that they would not be secrets any longer if they were shared with a congressional committee. His attitude antagonized McMahon who wondered how the nation could exercise any democratic control over atomic energy if the prime facts about it were to be the exclusive property of military custodians. On this issue the Atomic Energy Act did not represent a complete victory for McMahon. Civilian control of atomic energy was established but at the same time extremely tight security measures were built into the Act and special "Q" clearance was specified for those receiving information. This applied to the Congress and only the Joint Committee on Atomic Energy, a group of nine Senators and nine Representatives, could receive "Q" data. In other words, a rigid concept of atomic secrecy was carried over to the postwar period.

The second major contest between the scientists and the military thus ended more successfully for the scientists than the first in which Hiroshima symbolized their failure. When the scientists could marshal strength of numbers both within their ranks and among nonscientists they were a force to be reckoned with. Neither the War Department nor the Congress could afford to disregard their power. To no small degree this strength derived from a growing public awareness that scientists had become a critical resource for the nation's security.

However, the "victory" of the scientists in backing the McMahon bill was not won without losses. The initial display of scientists before congressional committees demonstrated that these men had feet of clay, and shrewd politicians noted the fact with some relish. In addition, the scientists showed that they did not have a tightly knit community ruled over by a single High Priest or even by a clique of leaders with one mind. There was great diversity in the loose assembly of scientists, and no one person could pretend to speak for all of science. This was to be confusing to the legislators who were accustomed to think of pressure blocs in terms of key personalities who were genuine spokesmen for their groups.

The Atomic Energy Commission, which the scientists had struggled so hard to create, took over the resources of the Manhattan Project on January 1, 1947. General Groves was relieved of his war-born project for which he played the role of postwar nursemaid. David E. Lilienthal of Tennessee Valley Authority (TVA) fame became the AEC's first chairman and presided over a Commission which included in addition to two others, Admiral Lewis

L. Strauss and scientist Robert Bacher. The latter, a quiet-spoken physicist from Los Alamos and the California Institute of Technology, brought a high leaven of scientific competence to the new agency. Lilienthal enjoyed the reputation of a liberal and the scientific community felt that it had in him an excellent choice to head up the new agency. The new AEC chairman looked forward to harnessing the atom's power for peace, but as the years passed and the Cold War fastened its grip upon the nation, he became disillusioned. More than any other person, Lilienthal might have helped to bring science and society into closer union, but such a closing of the gap never took place. The ex-TVA chief had been badly scarred by congressional harassment during his confirmation as AEC chairman and he somehow never managed to recover from the trauma. His administration of the AEC was marked by conservatism and deference to the military to the point where the AEC became a service agency fulfilling the requirements of the Pentagon. Under his rule, atomic secrecy fastened a tight hold on the AEC and despite his frequent assertions of the need for public information on atomic energy, the AEC behaved for all the world like an old-line bureaucratic agency.

At first it did not appear that this atomic secrecy would inhibit scientists very much in their discussions of atomic energy. Indeed, the provisions of the Atomic Energy Act merely established procedures for the new civilian agency, the Atomic Energy Commission. It was the interpretation of what should or should not be secret that became the critical problem and here the AEC leaned over backward not to antagonize either its watchdog, the Joint Committee on Atomic Energy, or the military. Atomic secrecy really became a political football alternately kicked by generals or politicians, and sometimes a real boot was given by high-ranking AEC officials, such as the very conservative Admiral-Commissioner Lewis L. Strauss. Perhaps if the arms race had not developed and the Cold War had not frozen U.S. policy on the atom, this overstringent secrecy would not have hurt public discussion in such a damaging way. But when the H-bomb became an item for public discussion—and it did so only after congressional indiscretion when

Senator Edwin C. Johnson blurted out the matter on a national television show—atomic secrecy interdicted the traditional means by which a democracy submits an issue to decision-making.

Much of Lilienthal's trouble could be traced to the Joint Committee on Atomic Energy and its eighteen men, some of whom were out to get Lilienthal's hide. Not a little of the AEC chairman's woes could also be assigned to the zeal of AEC personnel, who disagreed with his viewpoints and who turned to collaborate with defense officials and members of the Joint Committee. Lilienthal relied heavily upon the advice of a lofty, presidentially appointed body, the General Advisory Committee (GAC) to the AEC. The GAC consisted almost exclusively of scientists, mainly physicists, drawn from the ranks of the wartime bomb project. Lilienthal fell into the habit of asking the GAC for all kinds of advice. In any event, the AEC's science advisers occupied a special niche in the agency hierarchy, but like all such advisory groups they suffered from the part-timeness of their deliberations and from lack of responsibility. A weekend advisory group meeting every few months could not be expected to solve the AEC's problems— nor could a five-man Commission beset by internal strife and harassed by a belligerent watchdog—the Joint Committee on Atomic Energy.

Once Senator Johnson let the H-bomb problem out of the bag, scientists were at least free to talk about it, even though they were not all free to discuss it candidly. At least those who knew the classified data were restrained from touching upon certain technical areas. On the other hand, those who did not know the secrets could not be expected to carry much authority in public discussion. In any event the laymen viewing debate over the H-bomb would become very confused.

The scientists were agonized over the H-bomb decision. Unlike the 1945–1946 situation when they had a specific objective and an identifiable "enemy," in 1949–1950 their objectives were diffuse and hostile targets for their opposition were scattered. To complicate matters, most of the scientific community was hard at work at science and enjoying relative calm in their lives. Furthermore, the Congressmen were no longer easily influenced; their awe for the scientists had faded and had been replaced by down-to-earth realism. The Joint Committee on Atomic Energy had come to fame on a rising curve of atomic expenditures and developments; it was reluctant to deflate its own importance. Therefore it championed anything likely to enhance its own power in Congress or its public image, the two being very closely related. The Korean emergency touched off further waves of atomic expansion as the Joint Committee jumped on the arms bandwagon. Some of its key members were already deeply committed to armaments; for example, Senator Henry Jackson (D. Wash.) was such an obvious arms advocate that he was nicknamed "the Senator from Boeing." Such arms-oriented individuals were quick to seize upon certain technical developments, such as the small or tactical A-bombs, and with almost no opposition the Congress followed the lead of the Joint Committee and voted vast expansion of the AEC.

The debate over the H-bomb was afterward interpreted by the "victorious" Joint Committee as a black-and-white issue, the scientists opposing the development of the weapon and the Committee backing it. Actually, the debate was short-lived in this respect, since Senator Johnson broke the issue on November 1, 1949, and President Truman announced his go-ahead decision on January 31, 1950. Without arguing the technical details of the debate it can be stated that the scientists were concerned about more than the technical feasibility of making a weapon (in point of fact, the weapon proposed in 1950 was never built and had it been, it would have been prohibitively expensive to construct in terms of diverting valuable material from the nuclear stockpile). They were troubled that the nation as a whole was not assessing the impact of thermonuclear weaponry. Shortly after the green light flashed for the H-bomb project, J. Robert Oppenheimer exposed this problem:

It is a grave danger for us that these decisions are being made on the basis of facts held secret. This is not because those who contributed to the decisions or make them are lacking in wisdom, it is because wisdom itself cannot flourish and even the truth cannot be established, without the give and take of debate and criticism.

The scientists who pleaded for debate over the H-bomb were not asserting that they knew best; they were arguing for public debate of critical issues.

Physicists did not expect that the remorseless growth of the nuclear family would be abated on a unilateral basis. Their fear was that the arms race was running out of control and that high priority ought to be attached to exploring all possibilities for reaching agreement on control of atomic weapons. The pages of the *Bulletin of the Atomic Scientists* carried the argument over the decision to build the bomb:

Albert Einstein: The idea of achieving security through national armaments is, at the present state of military technique, a disastrous illusion.

Edward Teller: The scientist is not responsible for the laws of nature. It is his job to find out how these laws operate. . . . it is *not* the scientist's job to determine whether a hydrogen bomb should be constructed, whether it should be used, or how it should be used. This responsibility rests with the American people and with their chosen representatives.

Harold Urey: I am very unhappy to conclude that the hydrogen bomb should be developed and built. I do not think we should intentionally lose the armaments race. . . .

Arthur Compton: My reply is that in a democracy the ultimate answer to such a question rests with the people, just as does the right to declare war.

12 *Physicists:** This bomb is no longer a weapon of war but a means of extermination of whole populations. Its use would be a betrayal of all standards of morality and of Christian civilization itself. . . . There can be only one justification for our development of the hydrogen bomb, and that is to prevent its use.

* Statement issued at the close of the American Physical Society meeting in New York City, February 5, 1950. Signed by S. K. Allison, K. T. Bainbridge, H. A. Bethe, R. B. Brode, C. C. Lauritsen, F. W. Loomis, G. B. Pegram, B. Rossi, F. Seitz, M. A. Tuve, V. F. Weisskopf, and M. G. White.

As one surveys the argument over the H-bomb, it is clear that the men who were deeply troubled by the development were still the pioneers who had worked on the A-bomb. Perhaps there had not been time for the younger men to come to the fore, possibly they felt no deep sense of social responsibility, or it may have been simply that they were too absorbed in doing research. Whatever the reasons, it was the old-timers who continued to dominate the pages of the *Bulletin* and to speak in the public forum.

Edward Teller's plea was essentially that the scientists return to the laboratory and once again don the robes of the weapons-makers. This marked the widening of a chasm in the scientific community. In spite of their differences the scientists agreed that the democratic process of decision-making ought to be invoked. Unfortunately, they were all very vague when it came to prescribing a way to enlighten the American public on a matter so complex and technically barbed as the H-bomb decision.

Had it not been for Senator Johnson's outburst, the American people might have got no more wind of the H-bomb issue than they did of Roosevelt's decision to go ahead on the A-bomb. Even when something of the flavor of the debate within the halls of government distilled itself into the newspapers, the public had little basis for decision in the matter. Most of the substantive debate by the scientists reached print *after* President Truman made his decision. In retrospect there was little real public debate on the H-bomb issue. The H-bomb controversy did serve to throw the scientists into the limelight once again but they came off a poor second-best in contesting the issue with the authorities—in this case with the White House, the AEC, and the Joint Committee. There was division within their ranks and it must also be appreciated that by the winter of 1949–1950 Congressmen had accumulated some years of experience in dealing with scientists. The familiarity had begun to breed a measure of contempt, especially as Congressmen began to sense that the AEC scientists, whom they met frequently at committee hearings, could be persuaded to orient themselves along the Joint Committee's axis of inclination.

It is perhaps not fair to chalk up a defeat for the scientists in the battle over the H-bomb because they never really had a chance to argue their case in public. This defeat was similar to the decision to use the A-bomb against Japan. Unlike the situation in the previous two cases in the 1945–1946 period, the scientists now had no real unity. By the winter of 1949–1950 they were dispersed in hundreds of universities, defense laboratories, and research centers. Their community had no cohesive organization through which to voice effective protest. Individuals within the domain of science could, of course, speak as they pleased and dared, but to speak was an onerous chore, and the business of science itself required full and overtime dedication. Furthermore, it was exceedingly difficult for a young scientist whose views opposed those of a man like Edward Teller to win much attention. The Joint Committee on Atomic Energy and the U.S. Air Force fawned over Teller. In the strange union of the two cults of power certain individuals within the ranks of scientists became more militant than the most hard-bitten general. Teller was such a man.

Teller's profound influence upon U.S. nuclear arms policy might have been countered had an anti-Teller arisen to tilt with him publicly. The most likely candidate for this assignment would have been Oppenheimer, who played a big role in the scientist-military conflicts cited in this chapter. Dr. Oppenheimer had been on the "wrong" side of the scientists' fence in 1945–1946, but he had changed dramatically in his orientation since then, and whatever enchantment he may have had for the military faded and vanished completely when, in 1954, he himself was brought before the tribunal of AEC justice.

In a very real sense the Oppenheimer affair was a direct result of intercult feuding. The Pentagon, particularly the Air Force, was notoriously intolerant of "outsiders" interfering with its strategic policy determinations. Oppenheimer's mistake was to author certain sections of a report (Project Vista) which challenged the strategic doctrine of the U.S. Air Force. No criminal label could be attached to Oppenheimer for perpetrating it—this was the dilemma of Air

Force enthusiasts who championed the strategic role of that branch over the other services. It so happened that Oppenheimer's security dossier fell into the hands of Air Force officials who saw in his record of prewar associations and inclinations a pattern of conspiracy. But if the Air Force was the agent which loaded the pistol aimed at Oppenheimer's head, it was the Atomic Energy Commission which dispatched the bullet. In the clash of the two cults, one might have expected that a civilian agency like the AEC would have opposed the military. However, by the summer of 1953 strongly militant men were in charge of the atomic agency. Admiral Lewis L. Strauss took office on July 3 as chairman of the AEC, and on July 7 he ordered an investigation of Oppenheimer. Support for the attack came from the Joint Committee on Atomic Energy, a body once enthralled by Oppenheimer and now intent on his overthrow as a top government adviser.

The July, 1953, issue of *Foreign Affairs* contained an article titled "Atomic Weapons and American Policy," in which Oppenheimer spelled out the very philosophy that so antagonized his opponents in the Air Force, the AEC, and the Joint Committee. In this article the word "overkill" does not appear but a 100-megaton bomb is predicted. Referring to Russia's nuclear might, Oppenheimer stated: "The very least we can conclude is that our twenty-thousandth bomb, useful as it may be in filling the vast munitions pipelines of a great war, will not in any deep strategic sense offset their two-thousandth." The atomic expert clearly held no enthusiasm for the H-bomb as our salvation or for any margin of strategic strength as the basis for lasting security. But such views were blasphemy in the eyes of his detractors. As James Reston summed it up:

1. They suggest that a scientist, like a soldier, is expected not only to obey but also to show "enthusiasm" for Government policies, regardless of his own convictions.

2. They suggest that a scientific adviser can be punished by a security board for holding opinions contrary to Government policies.

3. They imply that the scientist's advice must conform to the Stra-

tegic Air Command's doctrine that the best defense of the United States is a paralyzing offense.

There is no need to retrace the agonizing ordeal of the Oppenheimer case. No defense which Oppenheimer might have marshaled, had he chosen to defend himself vigorously, could have extricated him from his dilemma. Only time could provide the substance of his return to honor. Though President John F. Kennedy invited Oppenheimer to a White House dinner, Oppenheimer did not gain clearance to act as a government adviser. In 1963, however, he received the Enrico Fermi prize, but a disgruntled Joint Committee on Atomic Energy sullied the honor by resurrecting remnants of the "Oppenheimer affair." By 1963 the two cults —the scientific and the military—previously so immiscible, could not really be separated one from the other.

The dominant fact of life in the Cold War was the annual expenditure of some $50 billion by the United States on national security requirements at home and abroad. When a nation commits half of its total federal outlays to defense needs, far-echoing consequences in its society are bound to result. And when the power of scientific research and development intruded itself so deeply into the apparatus and strategy of defense, it was clear that science could not remain unaffected by its revolutionary role. A cadre of young scientists who devoted their lives to defense research grew up in the United States. They, in effect, disappeared from the open world of free science by submerging themselves in secret activities. Such specialization tended to produce a group of scientists with pronounced military orientation. Whether directly employed in government service or by a defense contractor, the scientist-militarist risks a limited perspective and intoxication with promoting his own special field of competence. Defense industry or Pentagon protagonists may then use this specialist to advance their own cause.

This amalgam of science and the military is a kind of unholy alliance. One wonders if in the final analysis, the two cults of power are now so really different from each other. The interfusing of the disciplines has gone in both directions. In the Air Force today one finds colonels with Ph.D.s and many majors with master's degrees in nuclear physics. Some day, who knows, the Strategic Air Command may be headed up by a nuclear physicist.

Fortunately, the amalgam is far from homogeneous. The civilian superstructure of the Defense Department permits an inflow and outgo of civilians and a periodic change of management. A scientist like Dr. Herbert York, who served as the top-echelon science adviser at the Pentagon, wrote after leaving that post:

> Both sides in the arms race are thus confronted by the dilemma of steadily increasing military power and steadily decreasing national security. . . . If the great powers continue to look for solutions in the area of science and technology only, the result will be to worsen the situation. The clearly predictable course of the arms race is a steady open spiral downward into oblivion.

Dr. York's conclusion of October, 1964, was strikingly similar to that which Dr. Szilard and other scientists had reached in 1945.

During the postwar years scientists had given to the military power in greater measure than they could comprehend. One could, as Dr. York stated, add to this power—building up multiples of overkill—but the nation grew no stronger in its security. Within the span of two decades the architecture of defense was profoundly altered.

Although many scientists helped to create these changes they seemed curiously unmoved by their accomplishments. More bricklayers than architects, they pursued a steady course of collaboration in military aggrandizement, fashioning an ever larger and more grotesquely paradoxical panoply of war.

The public dialogue of the scientists about the proper control and use of nuclear energy, begun with such fervor after Hiroshima, augured well for a society that would become increasingly dependent upon science and technology. But for a number of reasons it spluttered into sporadic communication as the scientists retreated to their laboratories. Periodically they would emerge from their preoccupations, generally in response to issues which struck home personally or at their self-interest. Many of the younger men were making up for lost time and turning out scientific papers to establish a reputation. The pace of postwar research was much more rapid than a few years earlier and it was more demanding in execution. Furthermore, as science grew it fragmented into hundreds of specialized subfields. Old fields considered classical and stable— optics, for example—split into specialized sectors of research. New fields like solid-state physics sprang up and diversified into subfields very rapidly. Soon the natural sciences ramified into as many specialties as there are names for French vineyards.

The fragmentation of science was accompanied by suffocation. That is to say, the mass of scientific data published swelled to such proportions that it tended to suffocate those attempting to keep up with it. New periodicals arose to treat with developments in a single subfield. The scientist became more and more of a specialist whose full time was devoted to keeping up with events in his own narrow field. It became exceedingly difficult for an individual scientist to accept social responsibility for his work. Science became more and more a composite work in which a single scientist might contribute only a small part to the whole; the single scientist is therefore in an awkward position to assume a full measure of responsibility for its social impact. Moreover, scientists point out that the social consequences of research are often impossible to determine at the time of the research. The nature of much in science is such that even the most gifted expert cannot foresee the future. Einstein saw no threat to mankind in his $E = mc^2$, and Lord Rutherford, the first man to splinter an atom, had stated in 1933: "Anyone who looks for a source of power in the transformation of atoms is talking moonshine."

6

SCIENTIST-CITIZENS: THE BEGINNING OF THE DIALOGUE

Some scientists have spoken out and called for reforms in the patterns of national security. Foreseeing what lay ahead, they were conscience-stricken and, being so, gave voice to their fears. Considering the partial success which they had achieved, the odds were all against them; they had not anticipated that powerful support would come from a most unlikely ally—the weapons themselves.

The role of weapons-maker was not new for the scientist. Galileo and da Vinci invested their talents in military tasks for monetary reward. But in preatomic times man's discoveries and inventions did not magnify kill-power much beyond that which Darius the Great and Genghis Khan knew. Gunpowder, of course, brought about a modest increase in weapon lethalness but the statistics of aerial bombardment show that this was purchased at very great expense due to the cost of delivery of the explosives. The release of the atom's energy was revolutionary for the conduct of war because it allowed enormous explosive power to be packaged in an easily deliverable form. Furthermore, this package was relatively cheap compared to the equivalent weights of conventional explosive required to produce comparable damage.

Cost of nuclear explosives is not a reliable measure of their effectiveness. The Manhattan Project cost $2 billion. A warhead for a Minuteman or Polaris missile costs about $1 million each. However, each such warhead packs a punch of one megaton or one million tons of TNT—fifty times the power of the bomb dropped on Hiroshima. To produce damage comparable to that from a one-megaton bomb, some 8,000 "old-fashioned" bombs each containing one ton of TNT would have to be dropped uniformly over the same target area. The cost of such a bomb load would be many times that of the single H-bomb, but this is unimportant for the cost of delivering such a huge bomb load by missiles is so fantastic that no general in his right mind would think of using a TNT warhead for an ICBM payload.

That the scientist weapons-makers had added new lethality to war was obvious at Hiroshima; that they had produced cut-rate explosives was less apparent. Nonetheless, the combination of lethality and cheapness was truly revolutionary and it was this that so alarmed physicists as the Cold War tightened its grip upon the planet. Actually, they were concerned not so much about the A-bomb as about future developments which would make nuclear weapons both cheap and virtually without limit to their power.

The scientists felt a special concern because they realized that their professional training gave them an appreciation of weaponry the ordinary citizen could not match. This is not to say that all nuclear physicists became conscience-stricken and applied themselves to the problem of world salvation. The society of scientists embraces a wide spectrum of personalities as does any professional grouping.

The scientists who made the bomb were looked upon by the public in almost reverent awe. Men who could wrest from nature its most tightly bound treasure were, it seemed to many, quite extraordinary, akin to supermen. The public attention focused upon the atomic scientists together with the awareness of what they had wrought caused a number of them to begin a dialogue on the control of the new force. Bohr, Franck, Szilard, and others had already laid the groundwork for this conversation even before the first nuclear device was detonated. The specific problem of establishing a U.S. Atomic Energy Commission allowed for extensive public exploration of the control problem. The continuing evolution of nuclear weapons, especially the accelerated testing of more powerful bombs, put the nuclear experts in the limelight.

A relatively small number, well under one hundred, of biologists, chemists, and physicists pioneered in explaining the Atomic Age to their countrymen. As a consequence, many have assumed that these articulate scientist-citizens had been seized by a compulsive guilt complex. Analysts proceeded to explain the social behavior of these spokesmen as a reaction to the wartime "sin" of fashioning a new machine of death. Despite the widespread acceptance of the guilt complex as an explanation of the public behavior of the scientists, they did not engage in extensive "analysis." To my knowledge none of the "guilt-ridden" spokesmen of the postwar days required psychiatric treatment for such a complex. The scientist had a right to be worried about the A-bomb; it was in a sense his progeny. But more than that, it marked a bisection of history into two eras and the scientist knew that the preatomic world could never be regained. He was not necessarily affected with guilt; he did feel an active concern.

The author has in his files a number of carbon and dittoed copies of memoranda which were prepared in the course of "secret" discussions at the Chicago laboratory of the A-bomb project. Even before the formal organization of the Franck report, about half a year before the end of the war, a small group of atomic scientists began meeting behind closed doors in the Ryerson Physical Laboratory of the University of Chicago. Most of these men were young, although older scientists like Szilard, Eugene Rabinowitch, and H. H. Goldsmith attended the sessions. As I recall, rarely more than a score of people came to any one meeting. Almost everyone attending had a Ph.D. or would have one within a year. Since the laboratory could boast of close to two hundred such persons, the actual turnout was not very high. Szilard was the great memorandum writer and he redoubled his efforts as soon as it was possible to mention the word atomic bomb without stamping SECRET on the document. One such memorandum illustrates the motivation underlying the behavior of some of the scientists:

From the beginning we were aware that the scientific and military success of our work would bring new dangers and new possibilities of human benefit to the world. Until recently our work was clouded in secrecy. Now that success is achieved and the nature of our work is no longer secret, we believe that we should speak publicly of the profound consequences of the development. If these consequences are to be for the better, if disasters are to be avoided, it is necessary that every citizen come to appreciate the potentialities of our new mastery over nature. Only through such understanding can we hope that our democracy will be able to make wise use of the recent discoveries.

The document then formulated a series of questions as follows:

1. What would the atomic bomb do in a future war?
2. What defense would be possible against it?
3. How long would it take for any other country (besides the United States, Great Britain and Canada) to produce an atomic bomb of its own?
4. Assuming that international control of the bomb is agreed upon, is such control technically feasible?
5. What are the prospects of further development of the atomic bomb?
6. What are the peacetime possibilities of atomic power?
7. How would these prospects of peacetime applications be affected by control of atomic bomb production?

The passage of almost two decades makes it clear in retrospect that the scientists had a rather good anticipation of what would be important in the future. Issues relating to these questions have been in the forefront of national and world affairs—clearly a justification for the scientists playing a special role as citizens. Apart from the magnitude of the issues, their technical nature is revealed in the questions and goes far to explain why scientists felt that they had a role to play in public enlightenment. Dr. John A. Simpson, one of the leading young scientists in the Chicago group, pinpointed this aspect of the atomic situation. "On August 6 the bomb was announced," Dr. Simpson wrote, "and confusion began to spread throughout the newspapers and magazines in America. He added: "Only the scientists were in a position to dispel this confusion."

John Simpson might have added that the United States government was also in a strategic position to inform the American population and the world about the new nature of the nuclear era. The Atomic Energy Commission was the agency of government which should have carried out this assignment, but it evolved instead into a timid body afraid to say a word about weapons unless it double-checked first with the Joint Committee on Atomic Energy and the Defense Department. No AEC scientists could make a speech or publish an article without submitting a text or manuscript to official censorship. Presumably this process was intended to prevent technical data of a sensitive nature from inadvertently falling into Soviet hands, but as relationships between the AEC, the Pentagon, and Capitol Hill hardened, it turned out that the censorship was often dictated by political considerations.

Ironically, the rigid policy of atomic secrecy enforced by the AEC gave non-AEC scientists a place in the sun which they might not otherwise have enjoyed. Newsmen in search of a story would more often than not be rebuffed by the AEC. Its Office of Public Information became a joke among reporters and not infrequently when AEC officials did speak out newsmen were reluctant to accept their utterances as adequate. Under such conditions it was only natural that reporters would go to independent scientists and solicit their views. The relationship between scientists and the press also involved a great deal of education about the nature of nuclear technology. In the course of events, many reporters grew to have confidence in independent scientists and by the same token the latter came to know something about the nature of news.

The nuclear scientists' central theme was keynoted by Einstein not long after the war's end. "There is no defense in science against the weapon which can destroy civilization," he said, and added: "Our defense is not in armaments, nor in science, nor in going underground. Our defense is in law and order."

A rule of law under world government was prescribed by the

atomic scientists at a time when only the United States possessed
the bomb. It was one world—or none. David Lilienthal, a one-
time advocate of international control of atomic energy, looked
back from the vantage point of the 1960s and excoriated the scientists for their single-mindedness and for their naïve notions about
world affairs. "The physical scientists," he charged in his book
Change, Hope and the Bomb, "creators of the atom bomb, endeav-
oring to control their awesome creation, have sought a Single Solution to the threat of nuclear war in arms control or world government." Lilienthal himself had figured prominently in a plan to effect
atom control through the agency of an International Atomic Development Authority, admittedly not world government, but certainly
world law. Apart from his apparent change of mind, his critical
remarks would seem to indict scientists for their consistent advo-
cacy of a uniform policy on atomic control.

The nightmare of a nuclear holocaust was ever in the thoughts
of the nuclear scientists. Early in 1948 J. Robert Oppenheimer
warned:

> In this last war, the fabric of civilized life has been worn so thin in
> Europe that there is the gravest of danger that it will not hold. Twice in
> a generation, the efforts and the moral energies of a large part of man-
> kind have been devoted to the fighting of wars. If the atomic bomb was
> to have meaning in the contemporary world, it would have to be in
> showing that not modern man, not navies, not ground forces, but war
> itself was obsolete.

The United States plan to control the atom was laid before the
United Nations on June 14, 1946, when the United States representative, Bernard Baruch, put it bluntly: "We are here to make
a choice between the quick and the dead." He proposed the creation
of an International Atomic Energy Authority to control the development and use of atomic energy including:

1. Managerial control or ownership of all atomic energy activities
potentially dangerous to world security.
2. Power to control, inspect, and license all other atomic activities.
3. The duty of fostering the beneficial uses of atomic energy.
4. Research and development responsibilities of an affirmative char-

acter intended to put the Authority in the forefront of atomic knowledge and thus to enable it to comprehend, and therefore to detect, misuse of atomic energy.

The proposed Authority was, in fact, a global version of our newly legislated civilian Atomic Energy Commission. The United States was proposing to put atomic energy on a cooperative basis throughout the world. However, the Soviet Union gave this plan a frigid reception. Apart from the fact that the U.S.S.R. was asked to be host to foreign inspectors who would snoop in their factories and mines, there remained the fact that it was also asked to forgo rivalry in developing an atomic stockpile. As Congressman Chet Holifield stated: "The United States had a complete monopoly over atomic weapons and a virtual monopoly in fissionable materials. The preservation of this monopoly was a cardinal principle of U.S. atomic policy." The Soviets looked upon the American proposal as anything but generous and chose instead to develop an independent nuclear capability, signaled in August, 1949, by Joe I—its first atomic explosion. The atomic arms race, so feared by the scientists, was under way!

The American reply to Joe I was twofold. First, it triggered a decision on the development of the H-bomb. Second, it gave impetus to the U.S. expansion of its atomic facilities and a vast build-up of the atomic stockpile.

Some American scientists looked upon the decision to build the H-bomb as the national point of no return. They felt that now indeed the world was launched upon a dizzy arms race from which there would be no surcease. Others felt that now the task of seeking ways to achieve international control of atomic energy was more urgent. All understood that the world would not be frightened into seeking the ways of peace out of fear for the awfulness of nuclear weapons. No matter how murderous these weapons might be, it was clear that other nations would seek them out of traditional respect for power.

The dialogue on the H-bomb decision was over almost before it was begun. Scientists resigned themselves to the fact that weaponry would enter a new domain in which the explosiveness of bombs would be limited only by the designer's skill and the ability of vehicles to carry appropriate payloads to their targets. But practically no one expected that the H-bomb would become so cheap and so lethal a weapon.

Nature had given mankind some inkling of what was to come from the continuing exploitation of nuclear technology. The first note of foreboding was struck on the morning of July 16, 1945, when the *Trinity* bomb was tested at Alamogordo, New Mexico. This first test of a nuclear explosive dished out a basin of desert sand and turned it into brittle jade-green glass. Molten drops of sand impregnated with radioactive debris splattered over the desert floor in the crater region. This area was radioactively "hot" for some time. Winds aloft carried some of the debris eastward and a small amount deposited along the Wabash River in Indiana. This was later detected in strawboard made in that area and used for packing X-ray film.

A second warning came on July 25, 1946, when an A-bomb was exploded many fathoms below the surface of the Bikini lagoon in the far Pacific. The bomb was centered inside an array of World War II ships which were designed to test the effects of the underwater blast. I shall never forget the cascading fog of radioactive debris which enveloped the target fleet and coated the decks of ships with a mantle of persistent radioactivity. Very high, indeed lethal, levels of radioactivity were found on the close-in ships.

Both of these instances of residual radioactivity were produced by A-bombs of "nominal" size, meaning about the power of the Hiroshima bomb. Prior to 1951 a total of eight A-bombs was tested with a total explosive release of about 200,000 tons TNT equivalent of 200 kilotons. For the most part these tests had occurred in the Marshall Islands and there had been no alarm about any radioactive fallout on the North American continent. The first test of the H-bomb was scheduled for early November, 1952; the debut of this superweapon alarmed Dr. Vannevar Bush and in the summer of that year he visited the Secretary of State to urge seeking an agreement with the Russians not to test H-bombs. In his own

words, taken from testimony given in defense of J. Robert Oppenheimer:

> . . . I felt strongly that that test ended the possibility of the only
> type of agreement that I thought was possible with Russia at that time,
> namely, an agreement to make no more tests. For that kind of agree-
> ment would have been self-policing in the sense that if it was violated,
> the violation would be immediately known. I still think we made a
> grave error in conducting that test at that time, and not attempting to
> make that type of simple agreement with Russia.

Bush's proposal not to test the H-bomb was contained in a memorandum to the Secretary of State; the document remains classified,
but the above quotation is sufficient to establish Bush as one of the
first, if not the first, to make formal approaches to the U.S. government on the matter of ending bomb tests.

On November 4, 1952, General Eisenhower won a lopsided
Presidential victory over Adlai Stevenson. Three days earlier the
United States had exploded its first H-bomb—a signal event in the
Cold War which was to loom large in the Eisenhower years. The
superbomb was exploded on a sandspit in the Eniwetok Atoll. It
released an energy initially estimated at more than five megatons,
but later this figure was doubled. Unknown to the public, a severe
local fallout occurred on islands in the atoll; instruments located
there monitored levels of radioactivity which would have been
lethal to man. Fallout also occurred within the lagoon and one
group of test personnel was caught in a boat there but the event
was never publicized. The men were not seriously irradiated and
the experts in charge of test operations glossed over the significance
of the fallout.

All three tests added up to a grim warning that fallout should be
taken seriously when a bomb was tested on or close to the earth's
surface. It was on March 1, 1954, that the United States exploded
its *Bravo* bomb on a tiny coral island in the Bikini Atoll. On
March 11 the Atomic Energy Commission issued a terse announcement stating that twenty-eight Americans and 236 natives had un-
expectedly been "exposed to some radiation." The news did not

create a sensation, coming as it did when Senator Joseph McCarthy was capturing the headlines. However, an Associated Press dispatch speculated that the radiation exposure might have been caused by a "fall-out" of radioactive waste products from the bomb explosion. The world would have speculated for a long time about what happened at Bikini had not a tuna trawler *The Lucky Dragon No. 5* wandered near the test area, unnoticed by U.S. surveillance. The Japanese fishing boat was about ninety miles from the bomb when it exploded early that morning and the twenty-three crewmen aboard had been startled by the "strange sunrise in the west." Hours later, the fishermen saw the skies mist over and an eerie drizzle of fine, whitish ash coated the wooden decks and even stuck to the crew's hair and bodies. Two weeks later when the stricken boat put into its home port of Yaizu, the men presented a sorry picture. Their skin was burned and darkened; they suffered from malaise and some were terrified by the fact that their hair came out in clumps. A short time later the news reached Tokyo and then was featured on page one of the New York *Times*. Radioactive fallout was no longer within the security wraps of the Atomic Energy Commission!

Japanese scientists in Tokyo went to work on an analysis of the chalky ash which had been taken from the decks of the *Lucky Dragon*. While the Atomic Energy Commission refused to reveal the nature of the ash, the Japanese physicists and chemists soon found out about the nature of the superbomb which had been exploded. Incredibly, some American officials claimed that it was the chemical activity of the coral ash that had burned the *Lucky Dragon* crew. But, as the skilled Japanese scientists shortly discovered, the fishermen had been subjected to radiation damage produced by bomb debris from the *Bravo* explosion.

The H-bomb tests in the Pacific provoked political discussion, especially in Britain. On March 25, 1954, Philip Noel-Baker rose from the front bench of the Opposition and asked the Prime Minister to propose to President Eisenhower and Premier Khrushchev that further nuclear tests be suspended, pending discussion of control and eventual abolition of nuclear weapons. On March 30, 104

Labor members signed a motion calling for a ban on further experimentation with H-bombs.

While Noel-Baker and his colleagues took the initiative in urging the end of H-tests, we know that Bush had the same thing in mind and the idea had been discussed also late in 1952 in certain scientific circles. For example, at the Argonne National Laboratory, Dr. David R. Inglis and three colleagues authored a report, "A Specific Proposal for Balanced Disarmament and Atomic Control," which was privately circulated in government circles. The Argonne scientists drew attention to the need for the government to devote a substantial effort to planning for arms control and disarmament. Specifically, they urged that "a national agency and research project be set up for the intensive and imaginative study of arms-limitations problems" thus foreshadowing the creation of the U.S. Arms Control and Disarmament Agency. The Inglis plan did not mention test cessation specifically, but certainly any arms-control plan would have embodied limitation on tests.

Neither the government nor the American people seemed very much interested in arms control in 1954 when the Bikini bomb was exploded. The country was gripped by the frenzy of McCarthyism and the scientists were under attack. Oppenheimer's "trial" was conducted and he was found "guilty"—a verdict with which a very large segment of the American press seemed to concur. Secretary of State John Foster Dulles had enunciated his policy of "massive, instant retaliation" and the nation instinctively turned to increasing weapon power as a means of realizing a further degree of national security. In the State Department the word "disarmament" was synonymous with "weakness" and practically no one paid any attention to details of how nuclear testing might be curtailed or ended. This hiatus in planning for arms controls continued for several years and was to have profound consequences when at last the United States and the Soviet Union sat down to discuss the cessation of nuclear tests.

But beginning in 1954 something happened on the American scene which was to play a dominant part in making people conscious of the need for ending tests. Furthermore, it made many citizens consider the consequences of a thermonuclear war in a way that had not previously struck home. The phenomenon of radioactive fallout became a matter of public controversy and in the noisy, often caustic, exchange of words between the AEC and its critics alarming information spilled out into the public domain.

It must be remembered that the Atomic Energy Commission clamped down ironclad secrecy on the H-bomb. An article which famed Hans A. Bethe of Cornell University had prepared for publication in the *Scientific American* was yanked from the presses. Many copies were burned and the article was subjected to censorship by the AEC. Having seen the original article, the author knows that there were no actual violations of security involved in the publication; it was more a sensational act designed to impress scientists with the need for security. But the fact remained that the great majority of scientists, including a majority of scientists working for the AEC, did not know the nature of the H-bomb.

Had scientists outside the AEC known what kind of bomb the AEC had fabricated for testing on March 1, 1954, they might have raised a great outcry against the explosion of such a weapon. Their concern would have been rooted in the need to safeguard the atmosphere from excessive radioactive pollution. The *Bravo* bomb which drenched the decks of the *Lucky Dragon* with intense fallout was a "dirty" bomb in the sense that the lion's share of its energy came from fission of uranium as opposed to fusion of light elements such as hydrogen. Uranium fission produces split atoms, almost two hundred different radioactive species, which form a persistent source of contamination. Hydrogen fusion is a clean process in that no direct products of the reaction are contaminating. But *Bravo* bomb was not a pure hydrogen bomb; instead its explosion produced almost five hundred times as much radioactive debris as the Hiroshima bomb.

The twenty-three Japanese fishermen aboard the *Lucky Dragon* were victims of the intense concentrated fallout which the *Bravo* explosion deposited over an area of some 7,000 square miles of the Pacific. This fallout was in effect a preview of what an attacked nation might suffer in a thermonuclear war. However, Bikini was thousands of miles from continental United States and the American people might have glossed over the effects of fallout if it had not been for a drizzle of radioactivity which swept around the world, enveloping the United States itself in an invisible mist. Such fallout of global dimensions takes weeks, months, and even years before all of it descends to earth. Because of the complex nature of the many types of split uranium atoms in the fallout, the radioactivity is rapidly weakened by the passage of time. Thus despite the immense radioactivity released on March 1, 1954, the dilution of the bomb cloud in the vastness of the earth's atmosphere and the ravages of time robbed the remote fallout of most of its potency. By the time the fine specks of atom-impregnated coral dust settled on American soil, it added only slightly to the natural level of radioactivity present in the earth's crust. It was, to be sure, measurable and it was of concern to scientists, especially to those who worried about further contamination of the planet. But it was not a "health hazard" of any serious proportion. By the time the Atomic Energy Commission got through explaining how "insignificant" the hazard was, however, there was widespread public fear of fallout. The latter was a direct dividend of the AEC's policy of tight-lipped secrecy and "too little too late" release of information. It was one thing for the AEC to keep secret details of weapon design but quite another to bottle up information relating to the biological effects of radioactive fallout.

The role of scientists as citizens was sorely tried by the fallout issue. Clearly the scientist had a responsibility—to inform his fellow citizen about the facts in this matter so that an orderly and dispassionate appraisal of the issue could be made. But consider the plight of the scientist. If he was in the bailiwick of the AEC he was pledged to observe the secrecy provisions of the Atomic Energy Act as interpreted by the Commission. Anything he wished to say was subject to censorship. McCarthyism was in its heyday, Oppenheimer had been pilloried, and Admiral Lewis L. Strauss ruled the AEC with an iron hand. Strauss's behavior in the Oppenheimer imbroglio convinced many a scientist that it was worse than folly to speak candidly on fallout. It would be tantamount to mutiny aboard the AEC ship. As one highly placed AEC official close to Admiral Strauss observed: "If you disagree with Lewis about anything, he assumes you're just a fool at first. But if you go on disagreeing with him, he concludes you must be a traitor."

A scientist outside the AEC was by no means exempt either from the provisions of the Atomic Energy Act or from vindictive wrath on the part of the AEC. But he was in a most uncomfortable position of not having access to official facts. How could he speak or write authoritatively on fallout? In an age when most scholars solicit foundation or federal grants for support of studies, where would one find a benefactor?

The dilemma of the American scientist trying to act as a citizen was actually that of a democracy attempting to grapple with technology. The essence of our form of government was pinpointed by Pierre Mendès-France when he wrote: "Democracy implies a dialogue." Beginning in 1954 with the affront of fallout, American society was beset by the necessity for coming to grips with a new dimension in its national life. The nation had been silently invaded by foreign demons whose identity was known to but a few—and they preferred not to extend a dialogue to the people.

I believe that the U.S. press must be credited with forcing the AEC's hand on the matter of fallout. It mounted pressure against the agency as reporters became sure that the AEC was concealing vital information from the public. The Washington *Post* was a keen instrument in the attack on the AEC citadel and Herblock's cartoons on editorial pages of leading newspapers were devastating frontal assaults on the AEC bastions. The *Bulletin of the Atomic Scientists* featured a series of articles and editorials on fallout which provided the press with ammunition for a prolonged siege. As it turned out independent physicists made their own evaluation of the fallout problem, aided by technical assistance from Japanese scientists who analyzed the fallout debris on the *Lucky Dragon*. The AEC might be capable of censorship but it could not confine physics within its own domain. Thus scientists outside the classified area were able to make their own calculations and come up with data which were reasonably accurate. The publication of these data, largely in the *Bulletin of the Atomic Scientists,* presented a technical basis for assessing the fallout hazard. It was designed to be useful not only for the problem of assaying the biological risk of nuclear testing but, more importantly, for laying the groundwork for investigating the consequences of nuclear war.

It is to the credit of the Atomic Energy Commission that it belatedly published data on fallout, although details were held back for many years, but it could not refrain from superimposing gratuitous judgments of the biological risks. Here the AEC was the victim of its own policy decisions whereby it evaluated the biological risks engendered by its own testing of nuclear weapons. The atomic agency was charged by law to develop these weapons and it had been specifically directed by President Truman to exploit the possibility of an H-bomb. Prudence should have dictated that an issue involving a potential global health hazard merited referral to some authority like the White House where it could be viewed in full perspective. Eventually the responsibility for the health aspects of testing was assigned to the Public Health Service, but this was many years after the controversy reached its peak.

Public fear of fallout grew stronger during 1955 as radioactive culprits cropped up in new sites. One particular nuclear species of split uranium atom achieved great notoriety. This was strontium-90, a radiumlike poison, new to the planet. Strontium-90 has an unusual combination of characteristics which make it a most noxious contaminant when released in the atmosphere. As a radioactive material it has a "half life" of twenty-seven years, meaning that it takes that long for half of its activity to dissipate. As an element, it strongly resembles calcium and upon entry into the human body it "lays down" in the skeletal bone. There the rays emitted by strontium-90 bombard sensitive cells of the bone marrow and, if present in sufficient concentration, biological damage may ensue. The latter translates into bone tumor and cancer.

The bomb-to-bone journey of strontium-90 represents an involved and tortuous pathway, commencing with the formation of the radioactive species inside the inferno of a thermonuclear weapon. Complex physical processes convert this into microscopic bits of dust which are carried up into the stratosphere. Depending upon the place on the earth's surface where the detonation took place and the size of the explosion, the debris stays aloft for varying periods of time. When it finally descends it reaches the lower atmosphere and falls to earth along with rain, snow, or other precipitation. Taken up by plants, strontium-90 may contaminate wheat or ingested by cattle grazing on strontium-90-dusted cropland it may form a pollutant of milk. Once strontium-90 enters the human body it tends to lock into the bone structure so that gradually a person builds up a burden of the material.

Mothers in the United States were horrified to learn that amounts of strontium-90 were measured in the bodies of infants. Bones taken from infants who died of natural causes or through accident were ashed and studied for their strontium-90 content. To most mothers the presence of *any* strontium-90 in infants was cause for alarm; it did not matter how much was present. The fact that even the most skilled scientists could not state positively that there was a *safe* level of strontium-90 only increased maternal concern. The general public was distinctly disturbed by the fact that scientists did not know how much biological damage a fixed amount of strontium-90 would produce in humans. Laymen were used to thinking of scientists as precise knowers of truth. They were much confused when prominent scientists interpreted the data on fallout in disparate terms.

The Atomic Energy Commission attempted to justify its downplaying of fallout hazards by issuing voluminous data on the concentrations of various species of atoms such as strontium-90 in the air, the water, and a long list of foodstuffs. Dr. Willard F. Libby, a noted chemist and also an AEC commissioner, became the official spokesman on fallout hazards. Although an excellent scientist Dr. Libby had many deficiencies as a popular expositor. It seemed that the more speeches he gave and articles he wrote, the more undercut was the AEC party line that fallout posed insignificant biological risks. This clearly was not the eminent chemist's intention, but it was the end result nonetheless. He stumbled badly when he revealed the existence of a secret AEC project on fallout studies and blandly described it as Project Sunshine. He even invented the name "sunshine unit" to designate the amount of strontium-90 in human bone!

The currents of controversy which had been criss-crossing the public scene were alternately the result of interlacing dialogues between scientist and AEC official, scientist-to-scientist, and also scientist-to-layman. In the spring of 1956 a new dialogue was introduced by Adlai Stevenson, who linked fallout with a plea for a nuclear test ban. Stevenson's appeal came before he was named standard bearer for the Democratic Party in 1956 and it drew no vehement reply from the Administration.

On September 5, 1956, Stevenson restated his proposal to end nuclear tests; this time he appeared as a Presidential candidate before the American Legion Convention. Stevenson's campaign overture drew blood; President Eisenhower lashed back on September 19 with a caustic rejection of a test ban proposal, characterizing it as "a theatrical gesture." His running mate, Richard Nixon, struck harder and lower, calling it "catastrophic nonsense" and accusing Stevenson of "playing dangerous politics with American security." Thomas Dewey chimed in with a ringing denunciation, labeling the proposal as "an invitation to national suicide."

Why such furor in the Republican camp? A political campaign had just begun and counterattacks were to be expected, but the vehemence was striking. It was almost as though the opposition candidate had touched some nerves deep within the Administration. Stevenson believes that such was the case; he later stated that he had learned that a test ban was under active consideration by the National Security Council. This could have accounted for the Administration's counterattack; it would have been bad politics to admit that the candidate had suggested a line of action which it was proposing to back.

Never before in a political campaign had a technical issue intruded itself with such vigor. Charges and countercharges flew thick and fast. Scientists appeared on national television and radio networks to argue the merits of the test ban proposal. The Administration's hand was forced and finally on October 23, the White House released a ninety-item White Paper. The document revealed among other things that the Administration had considered a test ban as early as 1954:

Item 31. In late June 1954, after consideration of the matter with his top officials, President Eisenhower adopted an interdepartmental recommendation that the United States should not at that time agree to a test moratorium, but that disarmament policy review should be continued and expedited.

Politicians generally agreed that the test ban issue hurt Stevenson at the polls that November. But if the issue gained no votes for him, it produced a national bonus in the form of a public airing of a vital issue. Stevenson's defeat did not drive the hydrogen bomb problem from the political scene. As the *Bulletin of the Atomic Scientists* noted: "Scientists, in particular, cannot cease considering the world-wide danger of the nuclear arms race as the most important challenge to man." As a political candidate, Stevenson had shown the scientists how an issue, which they had been debating for many months, could command attention on the front page. It encouraged them to step up their own campaign of public persuasion to influence world opinion on the necessity for control of nuclear weapons.

7

THE PUBLIC
RESPONSE

If there is one lesson to learn from the handling of science and technology in the postwar period, it is that democratic institutions have time and time again been abused by government officials who deliberately refrained from carrying on a dialogue on important issues. Even the best-educated mass of voters is helpless if it docilely waits for issues to be presented to it.

The hue and cry about fallout, especially as it was amplified in the 1956 Presidential campaign, caused the Joint Committee on Atomic Energy to hold public hearings in 1957. At last the AEC experts and the independent critics were arrayed in public opposition; when the relevant data were displayed it became increasingly clear that the Commission simply did not have the facts to support its down-playing of the radiation hazards associated with fallout. But it was also clear that the evaluation of fallout risks was a highly complex problem. The congressional hearings served to point up the great areas of ignorance in many areas of the fallout phenomena and thus to stimulate research in these fields.

It was at this stage of the discourse that the famed Dr. Linus Pauling added a new ingredient to the controversy. The Nobel prize-winner from the California Institute of Technology was visiting Washington University in St. Louis on a speaking engagement. While talking with Dr. Barry Commoner, one of the most socially conscious biologists in America, Dr. Pauling got the idea of circulating a petition among scientists urging that bomb tests be banned. Within the course of a single day the petition was drafted, copies were mimeographed, and letters sent to well-known scientists in the United States. A few days later twenty-six men, some of them Nobel prize-winners, signed the petition and a chain reaction of letters was on its way. Two weeks later Pauling's petition bore the signatures of more than 2,000 U.S. scientists. On June 4, 1957, the document was submitted to President Eisenhower. It read as follows:

We the scientists whose names are signed below, urge that an international agreement to stop the testing of nuclear bombs be made now.

Each nuclear bomb spreads an added burden of radioactive elements over every part of the world. Each added amount of radiation causes damage to the health of human beings all over the world and causes damage to the pool of human germ plasm such as to lead to an increase in the number of seriously defective children that will be born in future generations.

So long as these weapons are in the hands of only three powers an agreement for their control is feasible. If testing continues, and the possession of these weapons spreads to additional governments, the danger of outbreak of a cataclysmic nuclear war through the reckless action of some irresponsible national leader will be greatly increased.

An international agreement to stop the testing of nuclear bombs now could serve as a first step toward a more general disarmament and the ultimate effective abolition of nuclear weapons, averting the possibility of a nuclear war that would be a catastrophe to all humanity.

We have in common with our fellow men a deep concern for the welfare of all human beings. As scientists we have knowledge of the dangers involved and therefore a special responsibility to make those dangers known. We deem it imperative that immediate action be taken to effect an international agreement to stop the testing of all nuclear weapons.

Pauling was taking a page from Szilard's book in going directly to the President, but in this case he had the great advantage that he could operate in the free air of a democratic society. Szilard, it will be remembered, had been constrained to restrict his petition to those within the secret area of the Chicago laboratory. Pauling had an additional advantage, but I doubt if he ever thought of it as such at the time. As a free-wheeling individual, Pauling had lent his name to the mastheads of quite a few organizations, some of which eventually found their way to the Attorney General's list of subversive organizations. Congressmen investigating un-American activities raised a great commotion about the Pauling petition, alleging that it was Communist-inspired and promoted. The Soviets began beating their propaganda drums for a nuclear test moratorium at that time, adding fuel to the controversy. I suspect that if Dr. Pauling had had no such troubles with those concerned, his petition would have attracted less attention. As it was, it received global publicity and scientists in forty-eight countries—a total of 11,021 signatories—backed the appeal. Pauling and his wife presented the petition to Secretary-General Dag Hammarskjöld at the United Nations on January 15, 1958.

It is interesting to analyze the reaction to the Pauling appeal in terms of the response it produced in various scientific circles. For example, he mailed the petition to every member of the National Academy of Sciences and a total of 105 signed it—one for every five members. The same petition mailed to 200 Fellows of the Royal Society, which is a comparable group in Britain, produced 95 signatories. Pauling estimated that of the 2,875 scientists in the United States who signed his petition, 2,500 were of academic background or came from research laboratories or hospitals. About 200 of the signers came from the National Institutes of Health, 20 were from the National Bureau of Standards and U.S. Geological Survey and 12—just one dozen scientists—were from AEC laboratories, meaning Argonne, Brookhaven, Oak Ridge, and Los Alamos. Only one scientist in the Defense Department is listed as a signer. Of those who put their names to the petition roughly 85 per cent had a Ph.D. or an M.D. degree.

Pauling received a total of 103 letters, each explaining why the writer had not signed the petition, and Pauling analyzed their reasons as follows:

19 approved in general but objected to some particular
19 were sympathetic but did not sign because they were not specialists in the fields concerned
18 gave no reason
15 said we can't trust the Russians
15 approved but did not sign because of some connection with the Government
 6 said that these things should be left to the politicians
 6 said they never signed petitions
 4 did not sign because Dr. Libby had said fallout effects were exaggerated.

Two letters from very famous scientists were received by Dr. Pauling:

Dear Pauling:

Thanks very much for your letter of November 6. I do not know enough about this subject to have an opinion.

> Yours very truly,
> (Signed ———— first name abbreviated, a world-famous scientist)

Dear Linus:

In reference to your letter of November 6, and to the enclosed petition, as you probably imagine, I couldn't disagree with you more heartily. I, therefore, have high hopes that you will fail completely in your undertaking!!!

> Best wishes, as ever,
> (Signed ———— nickname of a well-known university president)

To his appeal for ending tests, Pauling added an appraisal of certain aspects of fallout hazards that had not received much publicity. And he carried on a one-man campaign here and abroad whipping up popular support for his petition. To a certain degree Pauling fulfilled the role of anti-Teller but he could not match Teller's long experience and national prestige in nuclear weaponry. Moreover, Teller had access to the White House because his friend Admiral Strauss was not only chairman of the Atomic Energy

Commission, but special assistant to President Eisenhower. Strauss acted essentially as Eisenhower's science adviser and he saw to it that only those scientists favorable to his atomic policies set foot in the White House. This barrier was partially lifted after the impact of Sputnik caused President Eisenhower to appoint James Killian, president of M.I.T., as his special adviser on science and technology. Furthermore, the President's Science Advisory Committee was activated and there was a new flow of scientific viewpoints at the Executive level.

A Soviet proposal to cease nuclear testing on January 1, 1958, was advanced late in 1957 at a time when U.S. science policy was being given a new look. It is reported that when Killian informed President Eisenhower of scientists' views on a test ban, the President was genuinely surprised to hear that they favored such a step. Despite the fact that the issue was given new attention, the State Department still lacked the technical competence which, it was soon to become clear, was essential to negotiating a test ban. Nonetheless, there was a shift in attitude within U.S. policy circles and the Stevenson proposal to cease testing, viewed so negatively in the spring of 1956, two years later took on a different appearance.

On April 28, 1958, President Eisenhower revealed that the Administration was willing to discuss a test moratorium and he suggested that technical experts from various nations should meet to explore the possibility of agreeing upon conditions for a nuclear test ban. The Soviets agreed and on July 1, 1958, a Conference of Experts was convened at Geneva. Scientists from the United States, the United Kingdom, Canada, and France met with their counterparts from the U.S.S.R., Czechoslovakia, Poland, and Rumania. Suddenly scientists were cast in the role of experts, pinch-hitting for diplomats, who might lay the technical basis for an agreement to end nuclear tests. Many years of negotiation had failed to bring about a political agreement on the control of atomic energy and finally one approach toward moderating the tempo of the arms race appeared fruitful. Everything depended upon whether the scientists from the various nations could reach agreement on the capabilities of instruments for detecting nuclear explosions in violation of agreed-upon limits.

The technical problems placed before the scientists meeting at Geneva related to the sensitivity of instruments to detect and identify evidence of nuclear explosions taking place in four environments. Nuclear weapons might be tested at or about the earth's surface in the atmosphere as they had in the past. There was a considerable accumulation of experience in ferreting out such atmospheric detonations since the United States had a decade-long backlog of data from its long-range detection project. A variety of instruments had been developed for this special intelligence purpose. Acoustic detectors had been perfected to pick up faint reverberations of the bomb's air blast. Special instruments had been developed to measure electromagnetic disturbances produced by the bomb. Seismographs had been designed to detect weak earth murmurs resulting from shock waves which traveled through the earth. Finally, and most definitely, radioactive sampling techniques had been refined to a point where even a small air burst could be identified on the basis of the radioactive cloud remnants passing beyond the Soviet borders. High-flying U.S. reconnaissance aircraft sucked air into specially designed filters, which were then rushed to radiochemical assay stations. There, Geiger counters were used to measure the radioactivity of the filters and skilled chemists were even able to measure the power of the weapon tested and study its composition.

Detection and identification of air-burst nuclear weapons posed no real problem to the experts, especially if instruments were to be located on Soviet territory. One could arrange a system to detect and identify explosions down to a level of one kiloton (1,000 tons of TNT) or one-twentieth the power of the Hiroshima bomb. Admittedly, the problem of detection of weapons burst in space was very much more complex; one could test weapons so far away from the planet that detection would be a highly complicated problem. But at the same time the tester's problems were not easy by any means, and in 1958 the issue of space testing did not rank as highly significant.

Nuclear weapons detonated below the ocean's surface did not present unduly difficult detection problems, largely because of the homogeneous character of water. A relatively simple surveillance system appeared practicable for underwater nuclear bursts. But such was not the situation when the experts faced the problem of how subsurface bursts in the earth might be detected and identified. In the first place, U.S. scientists had tested only one bomb underground; this was the *Ranier* shot of September 19, 1957, in which a 1.7-kiloton explosion had taken place 790 feet below ground at the Nevada test site. Second, U.S. emphasis on test detection had been concentrated in a highly secret Air Force project which focused on long-range detection; data pertinent to seismic detection closer in to the explosion site were not sought by the Air Force project, nor did the AEC test experts pay much attention to close-in seismic signals. Here again one finds the nation's interests slighted by an agency which concentrated on weapon development to the detriment of fully exploring phenomena which could aid in reaching agreement on test cessation.

The basic trouble in reaching agreement on seismic detection and identification of nuclear tests arose because the earth itself is constantly jostled by disturbances taking place naturally in its nervous mantle. These small earthquakes produce a "background" of microseisms against which the shock signal of a nuclear event must be distinguished. Certain localities on each continent exhibit more seismic activity than others, and a nation might attempt to hide its illicit tests in such a region. The problem facing the experts at Geneva was a sophisticated version of "cops and robbers" in which each nation sought safeguards to be sure that another did not conduct clandestine tests. On August 21, 1958, the Conference of Experts agreed that an inspection system of 180 control stations, suitably located on the earth's surface, could police an agreement banning all tests above a 5-kiloton limit. This was a technical concurrence, not a firm political commitment, but it looked promising enough so that tests would cease once the 1958 series of the United States and the Soviet Union ended. The U.S. tests, code-named *Hardtack* I and II, included 31 shots in the Pacific, 3 space shots over the South Atlantic, and 18 Nevada tests. The latter included two kiloton-class underground shots, *Logan* and *Blanca,* conducted at the end of October. With a total of 52 tests in its series, the United States announced a moratorium on further testing, and early in November the Soviet Union did likewise. Perhaps, at long last, an inspection system might be built to enforce the moratorium and bring a measure of reassurance to the world.

These hopes were dimmed within two months when AEC analysis of its *Hardtack* data on underground shots led the atomic agency to conclude that the Geneva system was incapable of policing 5-kiloton tests conducted underground. Instead it appeared that the system would only have a capability for satisfactory inspection of 20-kiloton or Hiroshima-power tests. To bring the Geneva system back to its original capability would require a very large expansion in the number of inspection stations—a development which the Soviets viewed with little enthusiasm. The faulting of the Geneva system was a development in which Teller played a leading role, assisted by Dr. Richard Latter of the RAND Corporation, and championed by many in the AEC, the Air Force, and the Joint Committee on Atomic Energy. The enigmatic Teller nursed a deep suspicion that no trust could be placed in any agreement with the Russians and that any inspection system would have to be foolproof. The value of even a single illicit nuclear test was played up as contributing significantly to a nation's posture in the nuclear arms race. As the nation's most famed weapons expert, Teller had access to secret atomic data which greatly enhanced his ability to be persuasive in public, while not disclosing the data pertinent to his argument. He could always, if challenged, retreat to a sanctuary of nondiscussable information. For example, if the Geneva system as conceived by the Conference of Experts could work only for a lower limit of 20-kiloton rather than 5-kiloton tests, what would be lost by "allowing" underground tests up to 20-kilotons? This was a technical matter which, unfortunately, was never explored in public; under the secrecy which the AEC cloaked its tests and their results, the layman was excluded from glimpsing what the truth of the issue might be. Having fixed upon a 5-kiloton limit, the Geneva experts were in an awkward position to suddenly jump it to 20-kilotons. Their only recourse, at least in U.S. circles, was to see if the instrumentation could be upgraded to offset the nuclear statistics which the AEC had gleaned from its *Hardtack* tests. Belatedly, the State Department gathered together a group of scientists under the leadership of geophysicist Dr. Lloyd V. Berkner. The Berkner task force studied the detection problem and turned in a report titled "The Need for Fundamental Research in Seismology." The title itself indicated how far science had gone in effecting the affairs of state. It was not overoptimistic, but it urged that research should be undertaken promptly to improve the Geneva system and it indicated areas where substantial gains might be expected. However, the research would take time and money and it would require that an agency of government be assigned responsibility for it—preferably one which could develop enthusiasm for its research.

Responsibility for seismic research on nuclear test detection was given to the U.S. Air Force, the most outspoken advocate of continued testing! As it turned out, the Air Force was very slow to report on its seismic studies. Interrupting our chronology at this point, we may jump ahead to mid-1962; then, and only then, did the Air Force release the data that showed that there had been a serious error in estimating the seismic activity in the Soviet Union. The new data on Soviet earthquakes substantially altered inspection requirements, but the information was revealed after nuclear testing had been been resumed. Commenting on the handling of seismic research by the Air Force, disarmament expert B. G. Lall of Cornell University wrote in the *Bulletin of the Atomic Scientists:*

Throughout most of the period from 1958 to 1963, test-ban negotiators experienced considerable difficulty in obtaining data from defense scientists; annual expenditures of several dozen million dollars appeared to have borne few tangible research results in nuclear test detection. Perhaps if scientists working on such matters as the identification of underground tests had had greater motivation or encouragement from their superiors to solve the technical problems involved in disarmament and arms control, results might have been more fruitful.

The year 1960 had witnessed a number of negatively oriented events. Early that year, the "big-hole" theory of nuclear cheating was publicized by Teller and his cohorts in Washington, who included influential Congressmen. The "big-hole" theory, according to Dr. Teller, provided the Soviets with a means of evading a test ban agreement. The "cheater" would dig a big hole deep within the earth's surface so that it formed a spherical cavity. Then he would select the proper-size bomb, calculated to be harmonious with the dimensions of the cavity, and detonate it surreptitiously. Proper design in the dimension and depth of the hole would "decouple" the bomb's seismic shock so that as little as one three-hundredths of its energy would appear in seismic form. This meant, in effect, that the seismic signal was muffled by the cavity and that, if Teller's theory held true, a 1,000-kiloton weapon could be exploded and yet go undetected by a system with a 5-kiloton limit of detectability.

The Joint Committee on Atomic Energy, which proceeded to hold public hearings on test detection, appeared to be enchanted with Dr. Teller's "big-hole" theory. Scientists who argued that the theory was unproved and that the digging of appropriate cavities so far below the earth's surface would be a huge engineering undertaking were listened to, but it was evident that Dr. Teller had the committee's ear. It was no secret that the Joint Committee was in favor of resuming tests and it was therefore biased toward downgrading the performance of an inspection system. Pressure was building up in the United States throughout 1959 for the resumption of tests and on December 29 of that year President Eisenhower announced that the United States considered itself no longer bound to a moratorium, but that it would indicate in advance any nuclear tests to be conducted.

During 1960 a number of distinguished scientists formally associated themselves with the Democratic Party through its Advisory

Council and they strongly backed a Nuclear Test Treaty. They issued a report titled "Nuclear Tests and National Security" which discussed the pro and con of testing in terms of risks and rewards. Regarding the big-hole technique, the report stated: "It is estimated that the cavity required to muffle a 70 kiloton explosion would necessitate a two-to-four excavation program costing $25 to $50 million. Approximately twenty million tons of material would have to be excavated—an amount greater than the annual anthracite production in the U.S."

Even as the technical inspection problem for policing a test treaty was beset with obstacles, another aspect of modern technology commanded the headlines. A high-altitude aircraft, known simply as the U-2, was shot down by Soviet interceptory fire, and the ensuing fiasco strained Soviet-American relations almost to the breaking point. A shaft of modern technology had penetrated or rather overleaped the Iron Curtain, which had so long given the Soviets a sense of security through secrecy. And shortly, an orbital successor to the U-2, the Samos satellite, was to conduct an even higher level of photoreconnaissance of the "forbidden territory." Political implications apart, the new intelligence overview of the U.S.S.R. meant that its military strength, as measured in terms of numbers of deployed aircraft and missiles, was or would shortly be assessible as it had not in the past. The immediate impact of the U-2 overflights must have been traumatic to Soviet strategists, because they revealed a posture of military strength which was much inferior to the U.S. strategic power. Furthermore, with the worldwide knowledge that the U.S. intelligence had gained a new instrument for measuring Soviet strength, the Soviets had to reconsider their power status among the community of nations. The Soviets could tolerate a position of strategic inferiority as long as this posture was not advertised; but to be known publicly in this respect must have hurt their strategists immeasurably.

This sense of strategic deficiency probably played a very real role in Khrushchev's decision to invest missiles on Cuban bases. It was a bold gamble, but then some means of compensating for inferiority in bombers and missiles—and in having their sites known—

had to be taken as an interim measure. Over the long range the Soviets would have to rework the character of their strategic strike force, especially in the deployment of ICBMs in buried, hardened sites similar to those of our Minuteman ICBMs. But this would take time and—here was the rub—it would take a forward stride in nuclear technology to develop compact warheads for the new generation of missiles. Such warheads would in fact depend upon executing an extensive series of atmospheric tests, which meant that the moratorium would have to be broken.

The Soviets could of course continue to rely upon their soft-based bombers and missiles, but the risks of such a strategy were monumental. A strategic force which is exposed above ground with no protection against air blast can be destroyed by nuclear warheads hitting some miles off target. It can, of course, be used as a first-strike force, providing the nation to be attacked has no intimation of the onslaught. However, the attractiveness of an "out of the blue" first strike is very much reduced by two contingencies. First, if the nation about to be attacked learns of this action or is placed in a brittle crisis, it may itself be attracted by the appealing soft targets to strike first and eradicate the threat to its security. Thus in a time of international crisis, the possession of a soft-based or first-strike-only force could be a terrible liability. At a summit meeting it would leave its possessor no flexibility to impose his will upon another nation, since he would be, in effect, self-deterred. Second, granted that an aggressor might unleash a first strike with no advance warning, the technology of U.S. retaliation ensures that return fire will sour the fruits of victory. The U.S.S.R. would have to lash out with such a furious blitz of U.S. missile bases that the number of missiles required would be prohibitive if the American retaliatory blow was to be blunted. Furthermore there appears to be no military means to deal with the threat of the submerged Polaris submarine fleet.

In fact, the Soviet planners contemplating the feasibility of a first strike might conclude that a first order of business for them would be the production and deployment of an assured *retaliatory* capability. Defense-minded strategists would certainly worry about a United States first strike regardless of the past tradition of our democracy. Hard-headed Soviet generals would, accordingly, argue that they needed nuclear tests to restore a lost sense of security. This might be gained by developing compact nuclear warheads suitable for hardened missile installations, which could survive a first strike, or it might be aided by reaching for even more monstrous megaton bombs.

This discussion, simplified as it is, serves to illustrate the degree to which nuclear armaments impinged upon defense strategy and altered national security requirements. It would be whimsical to assume that TNT-minded military men in the Kremlin were quick to appreciate the nature of these changes. A tough-thinking general might well look upon the superbomb as just another weapon and long for even greater firepower with which to intimidate a foe. By the same token, we might expect to find similar military thinkers in our own security councils. American scientists were up against the task of persuading them that additions to the nuclear arsenal did not necessarily improve the nation's defense posture. Here the scientists were trying to hold back forces which sought to keep up with the arms race regardless of its tempo or of its true meaning for national security.

Pressure built up in the United States during the summer of 1961 to resume testing. The United States warned that if the deadlock on talks at arms control continued at Geneva, it would have to resume testing. On August 28, 1961, former AEC chief Admiral Strauss said: "I have no doubt that Russia has been testing all along," and publicly urged resumption of testing. Observers in the United States expected that underground tests would begin that fall at the Nevada test site. Then, on August 30, the Soviets announced that they planned to resume atmospheric tests of nuclear weapons; they did so on September 1. The lead-off test was estimated by American experts to be in the range of 0.5 megatons. The United States resumed its testing two weeks later with an underground shot at the Nevada range.

The world's largest man-made explosion took place on November 4, 1961, when the Soviets exploded a 58-megaton bomb in the atmosphere. This superbomb exploded with a power some three thousand times greater than that of the A-bomb which shattered Hiroshima. As its vast bomb cloud drifted eastward, it was picked up by U.S. patrol aircraft and samples of the debris were quickly analyzed. Scientists concluded that Soviet experts had deliberately jacketed their superbomb with a heavy coat of lead rather than uranium. Had the latter been substituted the superbomb's power would have been doubled, putting it in the 100+ megaton category. Such a substitution would, however, have had a potential double backlash for the testers. First, if local fallout occurred near the test site the split atoms of uranium could have posed a serious, even lethal, hazard over large areas of Soviet territory. Second, the worldwide scatter of dirty debris would have been inevitable and public reaction might have been extreme.

Why had the Soviets exploded such a huge superbomb? Did it have any military utility? If so, how would such a bomb be carried to its target? Experts in the United States have puzzled over the meaning of the 100-megaton bomb and most of them have discounted its military value. The new weapon, when perfected, would presumably weigh about fifteen tons and it could then be carried by a bomber. It could also be mounted as a nose-cone on a thrust-augmented Vostok rocket, but the rocket would be in the sitting-duck category, vulnerable to being knocked off its surface stand by a weak blast wave. Many analysts believe that the 100-megaton monster was designed to be an instrument of intimidation —a sheer exercise in brute nuclear strength and designed for its propaganda value. I personally believe that the concept of "peace through mutual terror"—to use Winston Churchill's phrase—leads to a form of nuclear madness in which terror-maximizing weapons hold a certain appeal to world leaders, regardless of military utility. But one should not overlook the possibility that Soviet strategists did in fact have a weird form of military application in mind—a hybrid type mated to mutual terrorism. Given a 100-megaton weapon, experts could either design a 1,000-megaton (1 billion tons of TNT or 1 gigaton) single-package weapon or engineer one from a multiplicity of smaller bombs. Such a colossal explosive, weighing perhaps two hundred tons, could be carried by tramp steamer or by submarine. It would not be deliverable by missile or plane, but exploded *in situ* off our west coast; it could send a vast wave of wind-borne contamination over much of the continent. Operating a hundred or more miles off Pacific shores, submarines would constitute a Soviet mode of "assured retaliation" which could be used for offsetting a military inferiority in ICBMs. This is however speculative, for our intelligence does not penetrate to the inner sanctum of Soviet weapons-planning.

If the Soviets had reasons for intensive nuclear testing which required atmospheric shots, the United States also saw the need for exploding weapons above ground. Early in November, 1961, President Kennedy ordered preparations to be made for such tests and, four months later, he went before a national radio-television audience to give the reasons for such action. He revealed that in a two-month period the Soviets had tested more than forty bombs and that "a primary purpose of these tests was the development of warheads which weigh very little compared to the destructive efficiency of their thermonuclear yield." The President even specified weapon powers in the 1- to 5-megaton range, a fact which fits in well with my speculation on Soviet thinking about the impact of the U-2. President Kennedy took pains to assure the world that our tests would "be conducted under conditions which restrict the radioactive fallout to an absolute minimum, far less than the contamination created by last fall's Soviet tests." However, no specification of the amount of contamination was given; this came over a year later when it was revealed that the total power of Soviet bombs tested in 1961 was 120 megatons, of which 25 megatons was of the "dirty" or contaminating species. The U.S. test series in 1962 had a total yield of 37 megatons of which 16 megatons were in the "dirty" category. For its part, the Soviet Union kept testing in 1962 with a total release of 180 megatons, one-third of which was "dirty"; thus the Soviets were the real "radioactive villains" of 1962.

The U.S. test program in 1962 added up to an admitted 86 shots and by the beginning of 1963 the grand total of all U.S. tests exceeded 260. The Soviets chalked up 126 shots which either we or they announced. France and Britain contributed a total of 30 more tests. The total explosive yield of all these tests amounts to 512 megatons or about 400 pounds of dynamite for every person on earth. Perhaps now, at long last, the nations of the world could feel that a condition of nuclear sufficiency had been reached in which neither the Soviet Union nor the United States felt at a disadvantage. By late spring, it became apparent that a test ban agreement might be within reach. For many months negotiators had argued over the degree of inspection required to investigate "suspicious events" as revealed by seismic signals. The Soviets held close to their traditional view of any international inspectors as tantamount to being espionage agents and adamantly refused to agree to a specific number of inspections on their soil. On the other hand, some improvements were made in seismic detectors and, as we have mentioned, the earlier data on the number of Soviet earthquakes occurring each year proved to be inaccurate and were revised downwards. These two developments tended to reduce the importance of having man-on-site inspections to look for evidence of test violations.

The deadlock between the two great nuclear powers might never have been resolved if on-site inspections had been insisted upon, but the art of compromise was practiced to produce a limited test ban, restricted to the three environments, air, space, and under water. All nuclear weapons tested were barred in these environments, but underground tests were permitted unless "such explosion causes radioactive debris to be present outside the territorial limits" of the testing nation. An agreement of this kind was initialed at Moscow on July 25, 1963, by representatives of the United States, the United Kingdom, and the Soviet Union. On the next day President Kennedy addressed the nation, labeling the treaty as "A Step Toward Peace" and urging full public support of the treaty. The stage was now set for a great national debate in the U.S. Senate, which holds the power of "advise and consent" under a two-thirds majority vote.

The President knew that it was necessary to drum up popular support for the treaty because a great many Senators had little enthusiasm for it. He knew also that it would be urgently imperative to apply political pressure to a number of Senators, including many in his own Party, if the ratification was to be won. For example, Senator Thomas Dodd from Connecticut had delivered fiery attacks upon a nuclear test treaty, enumerating a total of eight fallacies in it. Senator Jackson from Washington was known to be bitterly opposed to a treaty, along with many of his Democratic colleagues. On August 12, 1963, the Foreign Relations Committee under Senator Fulbright began hearings on the treaty. These continued for two weeks, during which time forty-five witnesses were heard and a thousand pages of testimony recorded. Nine scientists presented their views pro and con but the issue before the committee and the Senate was no longer dominated by technology. The scientists were listened to and questioned, but what they had to say was superficial; the issue would be decided by political considerations—by influence exerted by the White House and by the public. Grass-roots organizations like the Woman's Strike for Peace, SANE, and a multitude of church groups mobilized their resources and generated a groundswell of public opinion that was felt on Capitol Hill. A public opinion poll conducted by Louis Harris showed that 73 per cent of all Americans favored the test ban.

The attitude of the American people was all-important to the Senators as they debated the test treaty. As one leading Republican Senator observed to an associate: "Voting against the treaty would be like voting for fallout. The American people want a test ban and I am not going to oppose it." Other Senators, like Byrd, Eastland, Goldwater, Russell, and Thurmond were less sensitive to the mood of the country and maintained steadfast positions of unalterable opposition. To the nineteen who voted against ratification on September 24, 1963, the treaty appeared to be a move which would weaken our national defense. Many who voted negatively were known to be arms-oriented; some represented states where defense contractors annually won large military orders from the Pentagon.

On October 10 the United States, the Soviet Union, and Britain

formalized the Nuclear Test Ban Treaty. More than one hundred
other nations became signatories to the pact, but France and Red
China withheld their approval.

What caused the American people to focus upon a limited test
ban and to mount pressure against a reluctant Senate for approval
of the measure? Here one can only guess at the root causes for the
wave of support which was generated among the masses of Americans. It is difficult to believe that the words of atomic scientists
suddenly energized the U.S. population to demand some surcease
in the arms race. The valiant efforts of the scientists to communicate with the public should not be discounted, but it would appear
that the weapons themselves spoke loudest of all. People were
undoubtedly worried by fear of fallout and the continuing silent
shower of radioactive debris that swirled earthward from bomb
tests. To this they had a visceral reaction; the thought of air, water,
milk, and cereals contaminated by ruptured atoms was distinctly
unpleasant. This brought home to people in a miniature way the
horrors of a nuclear war which they knew would be immeasurably
worse.

President Kennedy's showdown with Khrushchev over the
Cuban missile crisis brought Americans literally to the brink of
thermonuclear war. No longer was this a hazy hypothesis of scientists; it was an abrupt reality and Americans recoiled in horror at
what might happen. Then, too, Kennedy listened carefully to the
advice of his scientific advisers and he more than once spoke out in
grim terms about the consequences of thermonuclear conflict. He
made official the predictions which atomic scientists had been
providing for many years. And throughout the upper echelons of
government there seemed to be a new awareness of the nuclear
era. In the State Department high officials realized that a continua-
tion of the arms race would involve the spread of nuclear weapons
to China, then to a sixth country, and a seventh, and an eighth. It
was impossible for rational diplomats to conceive that a world
abounding in nuclear powers would have much stability. In the

Department of Defense Secretary Robert S. McNamara, while not conceding a build-up of overkill capacity, planned for a series of cutbacks. In the Atomic Energy Commission plans were made under a Presidential directive for shutting down certain A-bomb production facilities.

All of these developments, more in word than in fact, seeped into the awareness of millions of Americans. It was a time of thaw in the Cold War. While the Kremlin might sustain a sense of strident aggressiveness on occasion, it was clear that the confrontation over Cuba had tempered Soviet policy. The signing of the test treaty symbolized a change in tempo of the arms race; it had not stopped, by any means, but neither had it been stepped up. The huge apparatus which both the United States and the Soviet Union had erected for imposing deterrence upon each other would remain intact and be periodically repaired. The sheer annihilating power of nuclear attack would remain the keeper of the peace, but no longer would it require constant aggrandizement. A point of nuclear sufficiency had been achieved by the two great nuclear powers.

A direct consequence of this nuclear plateau in weaponry was that military research and development could be redirected to other national purposes. The organization of science and technology for such projects as developing the ICBM, orbital systems, and the like was a postwar innovation of spectacular success. With the leveling off of defense needs, it became possible to channel this immense resource to new purposes.

The long dialogue which some scientists had begun before Hiroshima found the old campaigners close to trail's end. Some—to their surprise—had died of natural causes, from cancer and heart attacks, not from nuclear incineration. For two decades the world had seen no nuclear weapons used in anger. No accidents had precipitated nations into nuclear conflict, but the growing reliance upon ICBMs whittled decision time to minutes and made for a perilous peace. Some things that had worried and even frightened the atomic experts did come to pass. More nations possessed nuclear

weapons. Atomic bombs grew in power and in number. But somehow or other, even at what appeared to be seconds to midnight,
the world was spared a nuclear holocaust.

How much of this may be credited to the efforts of scientists is
difficult to say. My own impression is that they were very effective
in their persistence—in their single-mindedness, call it monomania
or obsession, if need be—in spreading the atomic gospel. But I am
inclined to believe that the scientist-layman gap was and remains
so great that we must give nonscientists much credit for translating
the scientist's fears into terms which the layman could understand,
even though very often the scientist deplored the text of the
translation. For example, Nevil Shute's *On the Beach* did not conform very neatly with scientific fact but it got a message across to
the average person. So, too, did *Fail Safe* and *Dr. Strangelove*. The
novel and the drama appealed to many millions of people who
would otherwise have had their lives untouched by the scientists'
obsession.

It was of course asking too much for the scientists to write
novels or plays, for their talents were of another kind. The scientists for their part had hoped for help from their fellow citizens
long before Dr. Strangelove enraptured movie-goers. Indeed, it is
puzzling to understand why it took so many years for Dr. Strangelove to put in an appearance. Perhaps this in itself is an index of
the separation between the scientist and the layman. If so, it is not
a good augury, for the need for scientist-to-layman dialogue did
not end with the signing of the nuclear test treaty. Nuclear science
is but one facet of modern science, no doubt a plane reflecting much
of significance for society, but other facets will dazzle the public's
sensibility.

In the years ahead a democratic society will be called upon to
make many cardinal choices on how science and technology will
serve the nation. These choices will inevitably involve technical
considerations even more intricate than those outlined in connection with the test treaty. Furthermore, consequences of choice may
be more difficult to forecast. Suppose, for example, a breakthrough

is made in the prenatal alteration of human intelligence—a possibility which some biological experts believe may be close at hand. Suppose, to be specific, it is found possible to upgrade human intelligence by twenty points on the I.Q. scale. How would a society such as ours exploit such a triumph of modern bioscience? Would the federal government subsidize prenatal treatment for all children? Or would this mental uplift be applied only to those who might be suspected to turn out to be otherwise mentally retarded? Or would such tinkering with the embryonic brain be outlawed through federal legislation? If so, how would our legislators contemplate the application of such a discovery in totalitarian countries? I suppose it is possible that if an American science team makes the initial breakthrough, it might be held top secret. So to speak, the biologists would have their own "A-bomb."

This may have a fanciful ring, but I suspect that our society is going to face a cascade of momentous decisions involving science and technology. It is no wonder that Dr. Glenn T. Seaborg has urged that "an informed citizen should be conversant with the larger principles of science, the dynamic potential of scientific research, the main contemporary currents of scientific effort and their relation to social forces." The atomic pioneer who charted the new elements lying beyond uranium counsels: "With such understanding, an intelligent citizen can make intelligent judgments between good and bad policy on scientific and technical matters. Without it, he can hardly participate fully in a scientific democracy." C. P. Snow more or less seconded this motion when he said: "Science will give us a better world only if enough people make sure it does so, which means that we must, to begin with, acquire the knowledge that helps us understand."

Educate the layman—this is the advice of many scholars who have looked at the gap dividing science from the rest of society. It is surely good and proper advice, but, I think, not sufficient to the task. If everyone capable of being educated in matters scientific could gain a grasp of the subject matter, I do not believe that the basic decision-making problem in our democracy would be solved.

It must be remembered that in the case of radioactive fallout the great bulk of the nation's scientists were almost as ignorant of the problem as were the specialists.

The dilemma of democracy trying to solve problems of a technical nature was pointed up by the French scholar Bernard de Jouvenal. He wrote: "Democratic government, as distinct from a democratic society, implies a confidence in Everyman's common sense, in his sufficiency for passing judgments on matters of general interest, and it requires the invigoration of Everyman's self-confidence in this respect." Confronted by the impact of the revolution in science and technology, de Jouvenal confessed: "Now the progress of science shakes my confidence in my own judgment."

Let us assume that all United States voters were college graduates with degrees in science. This is of course far beyond what Dr. Seaborg recommends or de Jouvenal would conceive of, but let us make the argument in extreme form. Would such an electorate be equipped to solve the problems arising from the impact of science upon society? Obviously the voters would be better informed on technical matters than they are now. But would they have any better common sense? For example, would they be better able to deal with the ethical issue of artificial alteration of human intelligence? In fact, would such an educated mass of voters be more adept at dealing with an issue such as the nuclear test treaty? My opinion is that while a higher level of education is desirable and would have some beneficial aspects (electing more qualified men to public office, for example) it would not heal the rift between science and society. A man may be a Nobel prize-winner in chemistry and be a political numskull with very little common sense at the polls. A scientist may have a Ph.D. in molecular biology and have little interest in or understanding of ethical issues.

Democracy places faith in the good sense of the citizen, but it does not, and should not, expect him to be an expert on everything. Voters would have no time to earn a living if they had to become proficient in just one or two types of expertise. Moreover, an electorate of highly educated people could be a passive population of specialists unwilling to foment issues. It is the airing of issues that lies at the very heart of democratic vigor and it is here that the expert must play a special role as citizen. He must help to formulate issues and bring them into the public forum. As Dr. Philip Abelson has observed: "We who have special knowledge and ability to judge values in science and technology should not be silent when issues involving us arise. Most of us have complacently played the role of tame cats and have no cause for recrimination when poor decisions are implemented. Unless scientists and engineers display more courage and take a much more active role in politics we are going to witness a continuing series of mediocre federal judgments in the areas of science and technology." Abelson could have added that issues need not have immaculate conception, but could and should be provoked by scientists and experts outside of government.

I believe that the tradition of democracy can be preserved even under the domination of science and technology, if we understand that the democratic dialogue is more complex than in prewar days. It is regrettable that the nature of our times makes it impossible for the public to understand much of science and technology. But this does not mean that a dialogue cannot be carried through on issues which are underlaid with a scientific and technical foundation. Those who are expert on issues which arise or are fomented need to speak out; this is the expert's first responsibility as citizen. He need not be an orator or colorful phrase-maker; he must raise his voice and express his concern. Then it is the responsibility of the rest of society to listen, to translate and to debate.

If the expert's citizen-responsibility is to speak up, to alert his fellow man, and to dissent, then it is the responsibility of the non-experts not only to listen and to act, but to protect the dissenter from the forces which are directed toward dissent.

SCIENCE
AND
8   CONGRESS

Senator E. L. Bartlett of Alaska recently depicted the predicament in which the Congress finds itself in attempting to deal with modern science and technology:

We have water research bills, fish research bills, mineral development research bills, urban psychological study programs, supersonic airplane bills, satellite communication bills, air pollution, water pollution, environmental hazard bills, cancer, heart disease and mental health bills, retardation and epilepsy programs, moose conservation and forestry research bills. Who is to tell the Congress what is redundant, what is necessary, what is duplication, and what is vital?

Mrs. Katherine St. George, Representative from New York, posed the issue with specific reference to the space program, which today costs about $5 billion per year. Of an appropriation for the National Aeronautics and Space Administration, she said: "I think that we have rarely had a bill that is more important and probably less understood than H.R. 7500. It is a bill that cannot be properly understood by any but a very advanced scientist. I do not think we have any very advanced scientists in the House of Representatives." Mrs. St. George could have made an even more sweeping appraisal of her colleagues, for there was then not one scientist in the House. The 1964 election injected one Ph.D. scientist into the 435-man House of Representatives.

Today the Congress handles appropriations totaling about $16 billion for the annual funding of research and development, but apart from the Appropriations Committees, it has no single committee which considers the research and development program as a whole. Instead, various R & D appropriations are gone over by a score of congressional groups. The latter range from old-time committees, which have seemingly little relation to the nature of the program they watch over, to postwar committees created to deal with some specific phase of technology which has assumed national importance. During the Depression years, research and development was not even dignified by separate budget status and the bulk of funds devoted to R & D activities came under the budget of the Department of Agriculture.

The wartime boost in R & D funds was, of course, sandwiched between the covers of a huge military budget. The $2 billion appropriation for the development of the A-bomb slipped through Congress through secret arrangement known only to eight members of Congress.

We have seen how the wartime A-bomb project forced Congress to set up an agency for the postwar development of atomic energy. The atom did not fit on the agenda of any existing congressional committee and so the Joint Committee on Atomic Energy was created. By this act the Congress entrusted its responsibility to eighteen of its members. No single group of legislators has been so long exposed to problems of a scientific and technical nature. Despite the ups and downs of elections, almost half of the committee membership chalked up a decade of service. Theirs was sustained experience and they were not bashful at their chores. The Joint Committee overlorded the Atomic Energy Commission, placing it in vassalage, and pre-empting to itself the promotion of United States nuclear policy. In an assessment of the performance of the Joint Committee, from the vantage point of 1963, James R. Newman, who had written the Atomic Energy Act of 1946, concluded:

When the atom business began, Congressmen and Government officials were overcome with admiration and awe every time a leading atomic physicist appeared before them and ventilated his views. The Congressmen never learned the substance, but in time they learned to use the jargon. We now have a group of so-called experts in the legislature who are no better fitted to weigh scientific evidence, no more able to distinguish professional knaves and mountebanks from disinterested and honest men than were the legislators of 1946.

On Newman's report card, the atomic legislators flunked the course. If his scoring seems overly harsh, it must be admitted that no test of nuclear knowledge has ever been applied to the Joint Committee. One would not expect committee members with only a high school education to conquer the problem of understanding the scientific aspects of atomic energy. But then a legislator does not need to be a nuclear scientist; the qualities of judgment and objectivity and fair-mindedness pertain more to the national interest. In these areas, members of the atomic committee have pursued an *ad astra* policy on nuclear armaments—more production, more bomb tests, and more of everything since the committee's influence grew with the AEC's affluence. The postwar growth of the AEC was tied to national security and to the tempo of the Cold War. The Joint Committee stubbornly resisted attempts to curb the arms race until public opinion forced changes in the atomic program.

The prime mover in the spectacular rise of R & D spending after the war was the Defense Department. In the last ten years about $50 billion have been pumped into military research and development. Combined with AEC funds for the same purpose, defense R & D spending accounts for two-thirds of all U. S. expenditures involving science and technological development. The Congress did not create any new committees to deal with defense R & D. This meant in effect that the Pentagon could write its own research and development ticket without fear of critical evaluation by the Armed Services committees on Capitol Hill. Congressmen were in no position to challenge the recommendations of the Defense Department; they lacked the technical competence to argue with the experts, who trooped into the legislators' hearing rooms. Furthermore, they found no mechanism to provide themselves with the kind of critical ability necessary for an informed dialogue. Their staffs were selected primarily on a political basis and they tended to behave so as to avoid clashes in the committee rooms.

Congressmen will rush to defend their positions by pointing with pride to voluminous records of committee hearings as proof of their assiduous efforts on behalf of the taxpayers. There can be no doubt that the printed hearings are of volumetric impressiveness. The House hearings on the defense appropriations for fiscal year 1965 number 3,136 pages. But as one studies the critical parts of the dialogue between witnesses and probers, between Congressmen and Defense officials, one observes Congressmen nipping at the edges of controversy, nitpicking over dollars and cents details or even frivolous minutia, but failing to come to grips with central issues, failing to challenge concepts and to relate different phases of the defense program. To read these hearings—an arduous chore which very few laymen and astonishingly few academicians attempt —is to appreciate the gap between the expert and the legislator in matters of technology.

Take, for example, such a vital issue as the determination of the level of strategic force required for nuclear deterrence. Granted that no magic number of nuclear-tipped missiles exists which is, so to speak, the "correct" answer; nonetheless, study of the congressional evidence indicates that the issue is not even debated qualitatively, much less quantitatively. This is not to say that the Pentagon has all the "right" answers and that this can be verified by appropriate grilling of defense witnesses appearing before legislative sessions. But the fact is that Congress does not even ask the right questions. It is to the credit of Secretary McNamara that he inaugurated the policy of preparing a lengthy statement of his views, including breakdowns of the sums requested for various defense missions. Even with this tidy itemization of the defense situation Senators and Representatives gloss over the fundamental problem of scrutinizing the essence of U.S. deterrent policy. Despite his decimal-point presentations to Congress, Secretary McNamara has fluctuated between two extremes: keying strategic bombardment to cities and to "counter-force" operations aimed at the enemy's military bases. These are two quite different missions requiring quite different numbers of missiles. Confronted with the problem, the Congress deferred to its aged leaders who instinctively veered away from a direct encounter, sensing perhaps that a careful and rational look at U.S. defense needs might engender slashes in the military budget. Congress has always been predisposed to vote for more, not less, defense and even with the enormous magnification of firepower which nuclear energy spelled for a warhead, a million-fold increase over TNT, it could not rouse itself from the spell of the past. Instead, the U.S. Senate witnessed a desperate attempt to add to U.S. firepower by forcing the Pentagon to develop new bombers—vehicles which defense experts knew could be no match for missiles.

It was Secretary McNamara, not Congress, who dictated that defense funds for research and development should be cut. This was not because more money could not be spent investigating new possibilities for weapons or because some improvements in existing weapons systems did not proffer themselves. The fact was that the great surge of technological effort of perfecting ballistic missiles had created a strategic capability which gave every prospect of being more than adequate for the near term, meaning the second half of the sixties, and even adequate for the early seventies. McNamara's confidence in the deterrent power of U.S. weapons systems was actually based upon a realization of their assured overkill capability—although he had to deny this for political purposes.

About the only politically agreeable way Congress found to respond to the challenge of the Nuclear Space Age was to create new committees. Legislators spend most of their committee time reviewing federal programs and activities with an eye to seeing if the taxpayer is getting his money's worth. By the time that agency programs come up for review they have been subject to multiple review within the Administration. For example, the Bureau of the

Budget exercises a strong control over the fiscal shape of agency appropriations requests; this extends to detailed item-by-item justification before specialists in the Bureau. Presumably even before experts from the Bureau of the Budget put a technical item under scrutiny it has been reviewed by consultants to the agency or even by an advisory panel of experts. The Atomic Energy Commission has a score of high-level committees and innumerable lower-echelon advisory groups, panels, and boards. Thus by the time a given technical matter comes before a congressional committee for study, it has already a formidable backup of technical review. Furthermore, if the issue is both specialized in one niche of science and is also classified on a national security basis, it may happen that closely held secret data are essential to evaluation of the matter.

How then does Congress burrow into the issue and get to the truth? Advice is meaningless unless it is listened to and understood, and Congress confronted some real problems in getting proper advice. It can request the agency experts to appear before an executive session of an appropriate committee and explore the matter. This technique is faulted by the fact that a scientist employed by a government agency is not apt to be a disinterested expert. It is only natural that, as an employee, he should manifest some enthusiasm for a program in which he is involved. But he cannot be unmindful that government agencies all demand steadfast loyalty to their line of interest. A scientist is apt to be pulled in different directions when queried by an astute Congressman or committee aide. He has a loyalty to his agency, but he also has an inner loyalty to science which demands that he be objective and accurate. Even if the scientist-witness is not in a government agency, he is still not free from the tug of these opposing forces. He may, for example, be a university man or a scientist-consultant to a government agency.

If a congressional committee listens only to agency scientists it may be inviting to its hearing experts with blinders. It may expose only one view of a problem and that a narrow one. Yet it is hard to find an independent critic who is both knowledgeable and courageous—and willing to take time out for a thankless chore. In some cases where the subject matter is specialized and classified, it is almost impossible to find an expert who is not already associated with the very agency whose appropriations are being scrutinized. Under such conditions the Congress is reduced to a rubber stamp in approving funds on the basis of parochial information. Or as expressed by Don K. Price, dean of the Harvard Graduate School of Public Administration: "Science has become the major Establishment in the American political system; the only set of institutions for which tax funds are appropriated almost on faith."

Does the Congress have no recourse except to provide a kind of blind endorsement to Administration proposals in the research and development field? Can there not be made available to it independent advice of high quality based upon careful consideration of scientific and technical ramifications of the specific problem? To my way of thinking the importance of the problem merits taking an approach which would clash with the traditional customs of the Congress. The legislative body would have to agree to reform itself —about as pleasant to Congress as self-surgery—by creating an independent advisory body to service its science and technology needs. Such a group might be called a Congressional Research Institute, a nonprofit organization reporting directly to Congress. I realize that there is little chance of Congress creating such an organization, but nonetheless it could serve a valuable function by having full-time scientists (preferably serving two-to-four-year tours of duty) to advise on R & D matters before Congress. Some of these advisers could serve on a nonvoting basis as members of R & D committees in order to effect a close liaison with Congressmen in day-to-day investigative activities. Congressmen might not, however, be able to tolerate the presence of scientists on various committees even though they had no vote. Their mere presence would be a constant reminder that the Congressmen themselves were not at ease in a technological world.

The legislators have, nevertheless, at least recognized that they need some advisory mechanism. To this end a Science Policy Research Division was created within the Legislative Reference Service but, alas, more window dressing than organic reform.

During the Civil War a number of technological developments led the Congress to create the National Academy of Sciences. The U.S. Navy was particularly concerned with the new technology of iron ships, steam propulsion, ordnance, and communication.

The Academy has no written specification for the qualification of its members but relies primarily upon election based on demonstrated creativity in research. Since election to the Academy is one of the highest honors which the United States bestows upon scientists, it is a coveted position and members of the Academy engage in their own political maneuvering to win support for the election of scientists who are friends or associates. However, the standards for election are exceedingly high and pure politicking is rarely successful in the Academy.

Karl Compton's plan to infuse vitality into the Academy during the Depression failed, as we have already noted, because the seniority-encrusted members could not rouse themselves to agree upon the necessity for change. There was little cohesion among members, who tended to regard the Academy as a place where annual meetings were held each spring and scientific papers were read. It has a marbled headquarters on Constitution Avenue adjoining the Federal Reserve System building overlooking the Lincoln Memorial. At the annual meeting, weather permitting, members would stroll among the magnolias and discuss the affairs of science. They were deeply concerned with science but they could never quite believe that the Academy was the agency to determine science policy for the nation. As stipulated in its charter, the Academy rarely took the initiative but waited for an agency of government to request advice. But prior to the war the Academy was not bothered much by such requests and such advice as it was asked to give often pertained to quite mundane matters such as road surfaces for highways, nutrition and standards. Many members felt that the Academy's most valuable work was the support of research through the awarding of fellowships to needy scholars. Despite its limited activities, the organization did have very great prestige value—an asset which Vannevar Bush recognized when he dealt with the S-1 project for the development of atomic energy.

Side-tracked during the war, the Academy seemed content to tend to its internal affairs and to hew to a traditional pattern after the war. For example, there is no record that when the Congress fretted over the control of the new force and the means to handle it administratively the Academy was ever consulted. Certainly, it did not enter formally into the argument which raged between the scientists and the military. Perhaps the Academy was being diplomatic because many of its committees included military objectives, and liaison with the Pentagon was essential to their functioning. Whatever the reasons, it held itself aloof from the strife over the Atomic Energy Act. This was a curious episode in the history of congressional relations with the Academy; it appeared that Congress regarded the Academy as a paragovernmental body to be consulted by agencies of government but not by committees of Congress. Did the Congress in fact recognize that the Academy might be caught up in an inner contradiction if it purveyed advice both to agencies of government and to the Congress which would then be called upon to judge agency programs? This question, unanswered then and now, had become more acute because of the role which the Academy has played in formulating goals for the U. S. space program—a point to be considered in detail in this chapter.

In its present form the Academy is a ramifying maze of some five hundred committees, subcommittees, panels, boards, centers, and institutes. These range from groups dedicated to highly scientific tasks such as one devoted to nuclear geophysics to a School Fire Safety analysis. The upper echelon of the organization consists of officers, counselors, and division chairmen who govern its activities. It is exceedingly difficult to evaluate the performance of the Academy as an advice-giver because of the sheer number of topics upon which counsel is emitted. It is however instructive to trace the role which the Academy played in giving advice on the U.S. space program since this illuminates the chaos existing in the formulation of science policy in the United States. It also illustrates the inability of Congress to deal realistically with a single phase of modern technology.

The year 1957 may be taken as the starting point for any discussion of the U.S. space program. It was in October of that year that the first Soviet Sputnik was shot into orbit to be followed within a month by a second satellite. Congress was jolted into investigative activity by the shock of Soviet success. Twin hearings were held; on the Senate side Lyndon B. Johnson headed up the investigation, while on the House side John W. McCormack conducted the inquiry into the space issue. A total of 108 witnesses was heard over the course of many months and some two million words of testimony were taken down. It is a curious commentary upon the National Academy of Sciences that its president Detlev W. Bronk never once appeared before either the Johnson or the McCormack task force, nor did any representative of the Academy give testimony.

By midsummer of 1958 the Congress passed the National Aeronautics and Space Act of 1958 and on October 1 the new space agency was officially in business. It inherited the assets of the National Advisory Committee on Aeronautics (NACA), which had focused its activities on winged aircraft ever since its origin in 1915. Beginning in 1952 NACA conducted minor research in space-related problems but as an old-line government agency it somehow or other never developed a very high regard for space activities. It was, however, an operating agency with nationwide research facilities and at the time of Sputnik's debut NACA had a budget of about $80 million per year. In the course of the McCormack hearings in 1958 Dr. James A. Van Allen, famous now for his discovery of the earth's radiation belts, testified: ". . . something of the order of $500 million a year will be required for a vigorous national space program." This was one of the few cost estimates made by a scientist for a national activity; it was to become an increasingly frequent happening that illustrious scientists would propose projects of multimillion dollar magnitude.

Science had clearly escaped from the penurious days of the past. This is strikingly illustrated by the precipitous rise of NASA funds:

Fiscal year	Appropriation
1959	$ 338.9 million
1960	523.6
1961	964.5
1962	1,825.0
1963	3,674.0
1964	5,100.0
1965	5,300.0

As one rereads the Johnson-McCormack hearings to gain insight into the skyrocket take-off of the U.S. space program, it is remarkable how little the testimony conditions one for such huge spending. In retrospect, the hearings had a short-focus viewpoint; they were intent on finding out how far behind the Soviets the United States really was and how quickly it might catch up. Both investigations laid heavy emphasis on the military implications of space as is evident from the fact that the majority of the witnesses came from the Defense Department. Only a handful of scientists testified, and there was no real attempt made to sound out the scientific community on its views. For its part, the latter seems to have been relatively unconcerned with the whole business. Indeed the Eisenhower Administration was a reluctant convert to space and would never have gone as far as it did had it not been for pressure from Capitol Hill. Left to its own devices the Eisenhower space program would probably have been on about the level recommended by Van Allen. It would have been a program directed along the lines spelled out by Maurice H. Stans, director of the Bureau of the Budget (1958–1960) near the end of his term of office:

(1) to seek knowledge about the universe through an extensive, well-ordered series of launchings designed to collect information on a very broad scientific and technological front;

(2) to find out how space can be useful to everyone through new applications.

In other words, the United States would have pursued a program of space exploration oriented along scientific lines—i.e., a Van Allen-type program.

This approach was altered when it became clear that the Soviets aimed at placing men in orbit. Project Mercury was launched to orbit an astronaut around the earth. Higher priority and more funds were assigned to this project in order to put up a good showing in the space race which more and more became a sequence of technological spectaculars. No men had ventured into orbit when John F. Kennedy became President in 1961. An advisory group of scientists which included Dr. Jerome B. Wiesner, the President's special assistant for science and technology, had turned in a report that was distinctly cool to the prospects for man in space. President Kennedy did request $126 million more for NASA than his successor, but there was no indication that a crash program for manned space flight was in the offing.

On April 12, 1961, Yuri Gagarin became the first man in history to orbit the earth as his spacecraft Vostok I successfully completed one trip around the world. This technological blow to U.S. prestige was followed five days later by the Bay of Pigs fiasco, the thwarted invasion of Cuba. The United States recovered slightly on May 5 when it profited from an openly televised launching of Alan B. Shepard, Jr., on a suborbital shot from Cape Canaveral. Although no official view has been given of the events which transpired that May, it is reasonable to assume that all of this played a major part in the decision which President Kennedy announced to Congress on May 25.

Addressing the Congress on a matter of "urgent national needs," the President urged a vast speed-up in the nation's space program. He summed up his recommendation:

. . . I believe that this Nation should commit itself to achieving the goal, before this decade is out, of landing a man on the moon and returning him safely to earth. No single space project in this period will be more exciting, or more impressive to mankind, or more important for the long-range exploration of space; and none will be so difficult or expensive to accomplish. Including necessary supporting research, this objective will require an additional $531 million this year and still higher sums in the future.

The Congress was shocked by this abrupt boost in the space program, but it proceeded to approve the additional funds with minimal debate. Presumably the Congress was sympathetic to the plight of a young President who had gambled and lost heavily on the Cuban invasion. There was also a deep undercurrent of faith in the defense aspect of space developments and the Congress seemed unwilling to argue the merits of a manned lunar landing by 1970.

Project Apollo, the U.S. effort to land a crew of men on the moon and return them to earth, spiraled in costs and accounted for the bulk of NASA's expenditures. At the present time it accounts for about a quarter of all U.S. research and development funds. And the total NASA budget is roughly one-third of all money which the government spends on science and technology. The sudden swerve in the course of U.S. research and development must be attributed to a high-level decision made within a matter of days and quite in opposition to the weight of advice from the President's science advisers. However, the President had a background of thinking about the moon decision which stretched back to his campaign days. In August, 1960, I was asked to prepare a critique of the space program and to list possible plans for the future. I itemized without attempting to indicate any choice three programs, the most expensive of which I estimated would cost $23 billion by 1970. The latter would fix upon the moon as the prime target for NASA. I was careful to point out that the decision to place men on the moon was "a political" determination and could not be justified on scientific grounds.

Oddly enough, the Apollo program did not run into criticism until its supporters tried to claim that it was aimed at scientific objectives. General Eisenhower had blasted the Apollo work in August, 1962, in an article in the *Saturday Evening Post:*

We have already demonstrated that in everything except the power of booster rockets we are leading the world in scientific space exploration.

From here on, I think we should proceed in an orderly, scientific way, building one accomplishment on another, rather than engaging in a mad effort to win a stunt race.

Eisenhower was later to characterize the Apollo program as "nuts." Despite the shaft of criticism hurled by the former President, his Party was slow to capitalize on the issue. In the spring of 1963 the Minority Policy Committee under the direction of Senator Bourke B. Hickenlooper from Iowa attacked the space program. A lengthy statement was issued which questioned the value of space activity as compared to other research. For example, the report asked:

Is it more important to have a man on the Moon than to conquer cancer which will take the lives of 40 million Americans now living?

Is lunar exploration more important to mankind than freeing ourselves from the tragic chains of mental illness, which now accounts for one of every four American hospital beds?

Is a fistful of lunar dust meaningful to the 17 million Americans, who, we are told, go to bed hungry each night?

Is a pathway to the Moon more vital than a highway system devoid of the slaughter which now claims 40,000 lives annually?

In other words the Republican task force was challenging the use of public money on the grounds that it could be put to better advantage. Hickenlooper's report was a basic inquiry into the proper use of science. This attack upon the objectives of the U.S. space effort did not make a big splash in the press but it did prod the Senate Committee on Aeronautical and Space Sciences into an airing of the issue. A number of scientists like Warren Weaver of the Alfred P. Sloan Foundation and Polykarp Kusch of Columbia University had expressed themselves critically on the space issue and they were invited along with scientists openly friendly to the NASA program to testify on U.S. space goals. It was rather late in the day, considering the work under way on Project Apollo, to begin examining such basic matters as national goals. One would have judged that this issue had been decided on May 25, 1961.

The cast of characters appearing before the Senate space committee on June 10 and 11 included: Dr. Philip Abelson, director,

Geophysical Laboratory, Carnegie Institution of Washington, D.C.; Dr. Simon Ramo, vice chairman of the Board of Directors, Thompson Ramo Wooldridge, Inc.; Dr. Harold C. Urey, University of California at La Jolla, California; Dr. Polykarp Kusch, Department of Physics, Columbia University; Dr. Frederick Seitz, president, National Academy of Sciences; Dr. Lloyd V. Berkner, president, Graduate Research Center, Dallas, Texas; Dr. Lee A. DuBridge, president, California Institute of Technology; Dr. Martin Schwarzschild, Department of Astronomy, Princeton University; Dr. H. H. Hess, Space Sciences Board, National Academy of Sciences; and Dr. Colin S. Pittendrigh, Department of Biology, Princeton University.

On the second day of the hearings, Senator Clinton P. Anderson, chairman of the committee, quizzed Dr. Seitz:

CHAIRMAN: Were you by any chance here yesterday?

DR. SEITZ: No, I was not.

CHAIRMAN: We had two people who, it seemed to me, were in favor of what has been going on and two people had some doubts about it and one was reasonably neutral. If space scientists can't agree, how do you suppose Congress is going to get along with the problem?

DR. SEITZ: Well, you have got a problem. [Laughter]

CHAIRMAN: I am happy to have someone recognize that.

DR. SEITZ: I think that most of you with a substantial amount of legal training ought to be able to cut through this.

CHAIRMAN: Well, Senator Smith and I are no lawyers at all. It makes it a little difficult.

Senator Anderson would have been in difficulty even if he had graduated *summa cum laude* from the Harvard Law School. No amount of legal training suffices to cut through the technology when equally qualified experts express divergent opinions. Abelson, Kusch, and Weaver, who had no association with NASA on a contractual basis, ganged up to question the priority assigned to space research as opposed to alternative fields of research. Scientists were at last debating the wisdom of spending one-third of the nation's R & D dollars on space research.

Seitz, as president of the National Academy of Sciences, represented that group and strongly backed the space aims of NASA.
He cited the recommendations of the Space Science Board of the
Academy, a Board established in 1959 prior to the founding of
NASA. Late in 1962 the Board issued a voluminous report titled
"A Review of Space Research" on the "current national program
of basic research in space and its future objectives." This was an
eminently scholarly analysis of the scientific aspects of the U.S.
space program, but unfortunately the basic research phase of
NASA's activities represents only a small fraction of its total expenditures. The real cost of NASA's program lies in engineering
and producing massive "space trucks"—the powerful rockets
which blast off from Cape Kennedy in Florida. This is by all odds
the lion's share of the costs engendered by Project Apollo. The
Academy's Space Science Board did not really attempt to appraise
the Apollo program in terms of what share of the nation's R & D
effort should go into it. Nor did it attempt to decide how much of
the nation's effort should be channeled into space sciences as compared to other sciences. Such a judgment could not be made by a
group of fifteen scientists who served on the Space Board. It would
have brought the group into conflict with scientists in the Academy
who would argue for greater priority for other fields of research.

In expressing himself before the Senate committee, Seitz appeared to give Academy endorsement to the NASA program.
Certainly this was the import of his testimony, yet as it transpired
the Academy members had not been consulted on the matter. No
referendum had been conducted to determine the consensus of
Academy members, although Abelson had conducted an informal
polling and found the overwhelming majority opposed to the lunar
program. Quite apart from the question of how well the Academy
membership might represent scientific opinion was the basic problem of the Academy's internal functioning. How did it operate as
an advice-giver to government agencies? Did this counsel in any
way disqualify it as an impartial adviser to the Congress? Did the
Space Science Board function autonomously within the Academy?
If so, was there not a danger that the Board was in conflict of

interest with itself because so many of its members were deeply involved in NASA projects? What was the specific relation between the Space Science Board and NASA?

Agencies like the Defense Department and the AEC have top-level advisory committees to give counsel on policy. James Webb, the NASA administrator, decided against having such an internal advisory group and asked Detlev Bronk to establish the Space Science Board to provide NASA with policy advice. The National Aeronautics and Space Administration contracts with the Academy of Sciences and provides funds for such advisory services as, for example, $300,000 for the 1962 study mentioned earlier. Some of the most influential scientists on the Academy Space Board have large NASA contracts, so that even granting their illustrious scientific attainments, some conflict of interest is involved. Without exception, members of the Board are space enthusiasts. They are also interlocked with NASA in their positions on various internal NASA committees. Again, we confront the problem of finding independent critical scientists to appraise agency programs.

NASA seems to have availed itself of the prestige of the Academy through its Space Science Board, soliciting advice on space science and then deftly transforming the relationship to apply to the whole NASA program of which basic science is only a small part. The Academy appeared to support the manned lunar landing on a crash basis. Seitz did little to dispel this impression in his (June 11, 1963) testimony before the Senate space committee. Senator Margaret Chase Smith formulated a series of penetrating questions about the NASA-Academy relationship but unfortunately these were not answered fully at the hearing. Partial reply appears in the fine print of a statement appended to the record of the hearings. The author and an associate conducted an informal inquiry among the key Senators on the Space Committee; we learned that a number of these men were very surprised by the testimony of scientists. One Senator said: "We never dreamed there was so little science in the NASA program." Most Senators were shocked to find that there appeared to be so little value to putting men in space.

Because man is such a fragile creature, uniquely a product of his earth environment and habituated to a comfortable level of oxygen, gravity, temperature, and *lebensraum* his accommodations aboard a space vehicle require a life-support system of one to two tons per astronaut. Lifting such weights off the earth's surface requires in turn powerful booster rockets and additional thrust-stages. These "space trucks" are exceedingly expensive and make the difference between a Van Allen space program using instruments for exploration and the tenfold more expensive present NASA program. Did the additional expense involve a commensurate pay-off in scientific knowledge? Here, of course, the opinion of the scientific community should have been solicited. The Senators thought they were doing so by inviting ten scientists to give their views. Of these only two had uttered any criticism of the NASA program prior to testifying and most of the others were associated with NASA in one way or another. The fact of the matter was that the Senators were really unable to find scientists to speak for the scientific community since the latter has only self-appointed spokesmen.

It took over a year before a statistically valid sample of scientific opinion was taken. In the summer of 1964 *Science* magazine sent questionnaires to 2,000 randomly selected members of the American Association for the Advancement of Science. Seven questions were put to the members, but to my mind the key question was: "What fraction of the total federal $15 billion research and development funds should be devoted to the space program?"

Based upon replies from 1,134 returns, 36 percent of the Ph.D. respondents estimated it should be 0–10 percent; 30 percent thought 10–20 percent; and 13 percent put the appropriate figure in the 20–30 percent bracket. Only 6 percent of the Ph.D. respondents felt that the space program should embrace more than 30 percent of federal R & D funds. Since NASA funds actually took one-third of the nation's R & D pie at the time, this meant that only about one Ph.D. scientist in twenty was in favor of the NASA program.

To my knowledge no poll was ever taken of the full Academy

membership. I did suggest this to several members but they felt it was not feasible. One member asserted: "It would rock the Academy boat." Even without a poll of the Academy membership, it is difficult to believe that the results would be much different from those of the *Science* poll. If I am correct in this surmise then obviously the Space Science Board is not representative of Academy opinion on the NASA space effort. Members of the Space Board may object that this is unduly harsh on them—that, in fact, the Board does not endorse the whole NASA effort in its more than $5 billion entirety. But surely the Board cannot be so naïve as to recognize that it is being used as a backstop for the entire NASA program. In any event the Academy itself has not made public any recommendation on the proper level of expenditures for space science nor has it indicated any specific profiling of the total R & D budget. In this connection, it is pertinent to single out two Academy reports which bear upon the issue of space funding and that of science and public policy.

On October 30, 1964, the president of the National Academy of Sciences transmitted to the NASA administrator a report on "National Goals in Space, 1971–1985." Seitz stated that the unanimous view of the Board was that:

1. The Mars program should be the major goal past 1970, starting unmanned with the Saturn class of vehicles with suitable decontamination.

2. The lunar program should be continued but subordinated to the Mars effort, recognizing continued lunar scientific goals.

3. A continued program of science in space is essential with respect to (a) Earth itself (b) Interplanetary space (c) Solar physics and preliminary exploration of other space objects (d) Astronomical observations outside the atmosphere.

This program is essential to the accumulation of basic information for manned programs. The development of standardized vehicles could reduce its cost.

4. The manned Earth orbital program should be developed for rescue, service of unmanned vehicles, and several military objectives such as inspection, but should be a secondary—not a primary—goal.

5. Flexibility should be provided in all these programs to permit exploitation of any major, unforeseen breakthrough or discovery. The Board agrees that our space program must satisfy all national objectives, but that to do this the scientific program must make a maximum of sense.

6. Obvious applications should be exploited quickly, as now planned.

The "on to Mars" advice of the Space Board in its 1970–1985 projection is highly parochial. Just what does the report (the six-point summary by Dr. Seitz is a fair summary of it) mean? It makes no attempt to assign a relative value to the Mars program in relation to other research or other space objectives. No costs are specified. A judgment is made of military objectives even though this is not within NASA's purview. It makes no appraisal of NASA's scientific program in relation to national space objectives. The text of the report recommends that "experimentation should be carried out largely by unmanned vehicles while the solution of difficult biomedical and bioengineering problems proceeds at a measured pace so that toward the end of this epoch [1985] we shall be ready for manned planetary exploration." This is ambiguous advice since a manned Martian mission will involve a tenfold higher price tag than Project Apollo. If the latter occasioned dispute how much more so would the national decision to send a manned spacecraft to Mars? Was the Academy endorsing such a project and, if so, on what grounds?

The Mars report of the Space Science Board accented the confused advisory role of the Academy. Apart from the flawed nature of the report and its lack of substance, it raised anew the propriety of the Academy in acting in a Delphian role.

Some backlash of criticism must have struck the Academy, for it organized a Committee on Science and Public Policy, something of an innovation for the Academy because it represented an initiative rarely shown in its history of advice-upon-request. Dr. George B. Kistiakowsky, a Harvard University chemist with a scientific pedigree extending back to research at Los Alamos, heads up the committee. Its first report, directed to the problem of human fertility, could hardly be called pioneering since the problem of overpopulation is not newly discovered. But it was a firmly worded analysis with straightforward recommendations. As the committee chairman explained the group's function: "The purpose is to take a look into the future and see what the needs are. Major fiscal decisions have to be made in determining how much support should be given to these (physical and biological) fields, and it is the hope of our committee that we can do a service for both the government and sciences by looking into these problems." While Kistiakowsky limited his committee's scrutiny to federal grants and did not encompass the whole R & D effort, it was a start in the right direction.

If the Senate space committee was bewildered by the conflicting advice it received from scientists and by the role of the Academy of Sciences as advice-giver, the Congress was equally befuddled in knowing what to do with the total R & D package. It had allowed funds for research and development to spiral upwards on a philosophy more of faith in its contributions to national security than out of generosity to science. But as the total R & D appropriation topped the $15 billion mark, Congressmen began to back off. The chunk which was made in the total federal outlays was too big to suit the taste of many a legislator; the R & D upstart had become too voracious. As fund-approvers the Congressmen were subject to a multitude of pressures, most of which were generated by powerful political sources. Money at their disposal could be vectored to dams, post offices, highways, airports, and highly visible public works which the public could appreciate. This was the stuff of pork-barrel politicking. Much of science and technology was new to legislators and either invisible or unreal. Many were inclined to believe with Francis Bacon that "Knowledge, that tendeth but to satisfaction is but a courtesan, which is for pleasure, and not for fruit or generation."

Furthermore, there were old-time members of Congress who liked to ridicule science and they could always be relied upon to find something outlandish about research. Virginia's apple-farmer Senator, Harry F. Byrd, could be depended upon to single out examples of foolishness in government research. On the occasion of his annual picnic he would mount the flatbed of a fruit truck and regale his constituent admirers with items culled for appeal to bucolic ears. He drew a big guffaw from picnickers when he read the title of one government project: "The Social Role of Aging Wild Horses." His reference to "An Analysis of the Sitting Areas and Pressures of Man" was rewarded with laughter when he revealed that "the average man's posterior covers 179.4 square inches and exerts 0.92 pounds per square inch."

Fellow Virginian Howard W. Smith of the House Rules Committee took potshots at research when he drew attention to a $31,000 item requested for the study of the biology of bumblebees. The venerable Congressman in his eighteenth term of office found it difficult to understand why the government should support a $64,000 study on man's resistance to persuasion. "Some thought Adam and Eve settled that question with the forbidden apple," he said. Science was fair game now that it commanded such a large share of taxpayer dollars. Legislators who did not understand it would take potshots at it. Those who thought they understood it would make their own decisions, perhaps of a more constructive nature. But whether of an understanding mind or not, it was Congress which had the final decision on purse-string letting for science and technology.

"In the last analysis," Senator Clinton P. Anderson said, "it is the collective wisdom of Congress itself which counts most in making important decisions. No decisions can be made in isolation, on a completely scientific basis, by disinterested officials. Congress will consider the scientific aspects of a proposal and pay attention to the facts assembled by the engineer. But in addition, Congressmen must ask some further questions: What will be the impact on our economy? What effect will the proposal have on our foreign relations? Will it contribute to the health and welfare of the nation?"

These are perfectly valid questions. But if the Congress is to display collective wisdom, a high degree of individual knowledgeability in matters scientific is presupposed. The over-all impression one gains in reading the committee hearings and in attending the public sessions is that such individual Congressmen are extremely rare. Thus it is essential that Congress receive good advice from disinterested and objective experts. Yet the mechanisms by which the various congressional committees receive their advice are inadequate. Intelligent members of Congress know that the apparatus of advice is obsolete and a number have urged reforms. The matter became of some urgency when the R & D budget intruded itself so significantly into the total federal budget that the Congress was forced to make choices. The turning point came in the fall of 1963 and was signaled by two announcements, one from the President's science adviser and the other from a member of the Joint Committee on Atomic Energy.

Speaking at the centennial celebration of the National Academy of Sciences (October 23, 1963), Dr. Jerome B. Wiesner said: "It appears then that the amount of research will be set by the willingness of the country to pay for it. Though we have not passed the point where we can fail to reap increased benefits from increased expenditures on basic research, we have reached the point where the rate of growth for the total research and development effort will probably be diminished." The President's science adviser warned the assembled scientists: "Serious questions are being asked and many of them reflect deep-seated concern about the character and purposes of the Nation's scientific and technological undertakings."

Congressman Melvin Price of Illinois was more blunt; he lectured that "the honeymoon in research and development is over." He urged a period of "very careful re-examination of Federal research and development activities." The veteran Joint Committee member was critical of the R & D community for: "1. Lack of clear-cut objectives; 2. poor estimating of costs; and 3. ill-defined management responsibilities." In particular, Price singled out the field of high-energy physics for criticism and promised a thorough congressional review of the program. His choice of high-energy physics was an odd one since if ever there was a field in which objectives were fuzzy, cost estimates unsteady and management erratic it is high-energy physics. How could one assign in advance a dollar value to an investigation aimed at turning up a new fundamental particle when this was completely unknown? Or how could one lay down a time scale for such pure nuclear adventure?

It was no secret that Congressman Price was upset by the rising costs of high-energy research and by cutbacks for atomic projects that he championed. After many years of supporting high-energy investigations, members of the Joint Committee were getting bored with the whole subject. There were little pay-off benefits which they could talk about to their constituents; talk of fundamental particles winged its way well over their heads. Furthermore, certain installations for high-energy research concentrated in a few geographic locations and this gave rise to quarrels reminiscent of salty pork-barrel days.

Dr. Philip Abelson observed (October 9, 1964):

Recent events suggest that a further evolution of the relation of Congress and science is under way. Research and development funds are likely to become a great new pork barrel. Indeed, such a trend is becoming apparent. Some who have analyzed the policies of the space agency speak admiringly of Mr. Webb's political adroitness in allocating facilities. It should not be astonishing that such a tendency should appear. Perhaps the amazing fact is that research and development was not made a pork barrel earlier.

The tang of the pork barrel hung heavily over the decision to locate NASA's Manned Spacecraft Center at Clear Lake some twenty miles southeast of downtown Houston, Texas. This was in the backyard, so to speak, of the territory cared for by Albert Thomas, chairman of the Appropriations Subcommittee on Independent Offices. The latter included funding for all space appropriations. Prominent Texans, however, credited Lyndon Johnson with being most influential in this NASA decision and the political significance was highlighted by President Kennedy when he visited Texas and defined the nation's space aims. Mixed with the inventory of reasons for Project Apollo was the dollar-flow which would go to residents of Texas. Some suspicious souls implied that cause and effect might have a political relation in the President's decision on the moon project. The political fallout from the Apollo program may be summarized as follows:

300,000 persons employed on the space mission by 1965
8 states awarded contracts of more than $50 million

23 additional states given awards in excess of $1 million
$500 million in facilities built in Mississippi
$350 million in facilities constructed in Texas
$419 million contract to Boeing Company for Saturn booster

Senator Wallace Bennett phrased space statistics in a more down-to-earth manner in arguing for more contracts for his home state of Utah. He pointed out that the space budget amounted to only 20 cents per person so far as its pay-off to Utah was concerned, whereas Texas garnered $25 for each of its residents and California took first place with $143 per person.

The U.S. aerospace industry was headed into decline after the last B-52 rolled off the production line and hopes faded for the B-70 bomber. To be sure there were impressive numbers of ICBMs to be built, but once the research and development was done, the production costs (and corporate profits) were much lower for missiles than for bombers. Furthermore, the "spare" orders for replacement parts were always a big bonus for an aircraft manufacturer but these meant little for a missile which would in effect "fly" only once. It did not deteriorate much standing in its underground silo. Thus when President Kennedy made his decision on Project Apollo it was most welcome news to the ailing aerospace industry. A number of aerospace companies had seen or were about to witness their stocks nosedive on the market. Even with the massive infusion of space funds by NASA and to a lesser extent by the Defense Department, many of these companies have been depressed by the lack of business. Political leaders cannot be unmindful of the danger at the polls when workers go idle and plants run at reduced schedules. For this reason, if for no other, the United States will not suddenly alter its Apollo plans; the economic consequences would be too repercussive.

The change in the R & D weather was accompanied by a concerted move in the House of Representatives to re-examine the nation's research activities, their scope, conduct, and cost. Carl Elliott of Alabama, subsequently knocked out of office in the primaries, headed up a Select Committee on Government Research which included key Congressmen from other House committees concerned with research. Understandably none of these gentlemen was anxious to see the fortunes of his respective committee decline, and his cooperation with the chairman was one of cautious participation. So jealous of its own prerogatives was the House space committee under its seventy-two-year-old chairman George Miller of California that it established its own review task force. The Elliott committee amassed a considerable amount of testimony and statistical data, but the political demise of its chairman foredoomed it to tedium. If Congress was to put its R & D house in order some more potent effort would be required.

A show of scientific advisory strength was attempted by the House space committee when it put together a group of distinguished scientists to act as R & D consultants. The advisers are put on public display for one day each year, but as one of them told the author: "The committee doesn't really work us." In this respect many advisory committees share the same fault—that of part-time experts who come to Washington long enough to glimpse the problem but not long enough to really educate those who need advice.

In sum, the legislators failed to appreciate the quality of the revolutionary change which modern science and technology had wrought in the postwar world. Individually, some Congressmen did understand that the rip tide of technology had swept away the old landmarks, but they were in the very small minority and seldom the senior lawmakers, who dominate committees through seniority-awarded chairmanships. Powerful chairmen can and do exercise complete control over committee business. But some of these men completed their education two generations ago. Needless to say, an understanding of modern science is difficult with the added burden of age.

9

SCIENTISTS
AND
POLITICS

The emergence of science as a potent factor in the federal budget made it inevitable that scientists would be drawn into the political vortex. Wallace S. Sayre, Columbia University professor of public administration, put it this way:

The scientists are now inescapably committed to politics if they hope to exercise influence in the shaping of public policy, including science policy. The leaders of the scientists, then, are perforce politicians. As politicians in a democratic order, they are effective in the degree to which they understand the political process, accept its rules, and play their part in the process with more candor than piety, accepting gladly the fact that they are in the battle rather than above it.

Einstein injected himself into politics when he sent his A-bomb letter directly to President Roosevelt. The atomic scientists like Szilard and Franck intervened in a secret dialogue over the decision to use the A-bomb. And the scientists engaged in the political process when they lobbied for the civilian control of atomic energy.

Given large federal commitments to research and development it was natural for science and politics to become deeply intertwined. Einstein in a very real sense was the true innovator here although he did not personally regard himself as mixed up in politics. Shortly after Hiroshima he wrote: "As far as we, the physicists, are concerned, we are no politicians and it has never been our wish to meddle in politics." But the fact is that Einstein and many other scientists *did* meddle in politics. Not of course in the crude sense of the word; but nevertheless, once the A-bomb was a reality, the scientists commanded political power. When an Einstein or a Urey expressed an opinion on the bomb this could have wide repercussions. The massive involvement of science with federal support also made it inevitable that scientists and politicians would be rubbing elbows. The traditional "pork barrel" might take on some strange shapes but it would still smell the same to legislators. The bigness of science brought science within the orbit of government and challenged its independence.

Scientists took political action for the first time along party lines in 1959. Paul M. Butler, chairman of the Democratic National Committee, announced that a seventeen-member Advisory Committee on Science and Technology had been appointed to work with the Democratic Advisory Council. In announcing the formation of the group, Butler said:

The Democratic Advisory Council authorized the Committee because it recognizes that science and technology should play an enormous role in the formulation of virtually all aspects of government policy ranging from national defense and foreign affairs to our economic and physical well-being. Our Party believes that our recommendations concerning legislative and administrative actions must be arrived at with full knowledge of the scientific and technological aspects of the problems which confront us. The Council feels that the scientific community has not been consulted sufficiently on national policies in the past six years and has been listened to even less. We want Democratic policies to be as sound as possible from the scientific and technological points of view.

It will be recalled that the Democratic Advisory Council was a "shadow cabinet" including influential politicians like Truman, Stevenson, Lehman, and Harriman. It included statesmen of the caliber of Dean Acheson and brains of men like Kenneth Galbraith. The Council represented a competitive locus of power to the congressional leaders like Sam Rayburn and Lyndon Johnson, both of whom opposed it bitterly. Other congressional figures in the Democratic Party supported the Council but looked upon the scientists as intruders upon the political scene. To be sure, the ways of a politician and of a scientist are quite dissimilar. A scientist is disciplined to respect the truth and to seek it dispassionately. A politician practices the art of compromise; he is a master blender of divergent opinions and a healer of rifts. A scientist is by nature an innovator, delighting in that which is new, and in these ways he is a revolutionary. A politician innovates usually out of desperation; he seeks the tried and true—that which he understands. Thus it was interesting to see how the scientists and politicians would get along with each other.

Had the scientists behaved in a brash manner they might have been resented by the members of the Democratic Advisory Council. In a statement labeled "Science and Politics," the scientists made clear their advisory role: "We feel that the citizen-scientist has a responsibility to think about the problems of science and society and to communicate his thoughts to those who can convert ideas into the fabric of national policy. Politicians are faced with issues which often embrace highly complex facets of modern technology; here the scientist can give valuable technical advice." But the scientists emphasized that they would not be politicians in their service to the Council: "It is not intended that the new Committee prepare or issue public statements for purely political purposes. . . . scientific and technological facts should not be the property of any political party."

The scientists' committee was headed by Dr. Ernest Pollard, a Yale University biophysicist, who had demonstrated his political courage when he undertook his own investigation of the alleged security scandals at Fort Monmouth during Senator McCarthy's heyday. His calm and objective assembly of the facts in this case resulted in an impressive document which effectively answered McCarthy's wild charges against the scientists. The full composition of the committee was as follows: Samuel K. Allison, Enrico Fermi Institute, University of Chicago; Harrison S. Brown, California Institute of Technology; Leslie C. Dunn, Columbia University; Louis B. Flexner, University of Pennsylvania; Trevor Gardner, Hycon Manufacturing Company; H. Bentley Glass, Johns Hopkins University; David R. Goddard, University of Pennsylvania; Dr. Frank Goddard,* Jet Propulsion Laboratory; David L. Hill, consulting physicist, New York City; Polykarp Kusch, Columbia University; Charles C. Lauritsen,* California Institute of Technology; Frank T. McClure, Applied Physics Laboratory; Richard B. Roberts, Carnegie Institution of Washington; John S. Toll, University of Maryland; Harold C. Urey, University of California; Gilbert F. White, University of Chicago.

Scientific fields covered by the scientists included physics, genetics, botany, anatomy, biophysics, zoology, geochemistry, engineering, and geography. Charles Tyroler, II, the executive director of the Democratic Advisory Council, worked closely with the scientists and brought to them an awareness of how politicians thought about their problems. He did much to smooth relations between the scientists and politicians to the extent that their unlike worlds were successfully joined. Scientists and politicians were to be found working together over drafts of reports and relaxing at cocktail parties and after hours at evening sessions.

The author can attest to the labors of the scientists because he has in his files all the drafts and notes of the many reports which the committee prepared. The breadth of the scientists' interests and concerns is illustrated by the following inventory of committee agenda:

1. The relation of science to national defense policy.

2. Formulation of an adequate national science policy.

3. Formulation of legislation to promote the free exchange of non-secret data between nations.

4. Steps to permit freer communication between U.S. and foreign scientists and engineers; encouragement of international conferences in the U.S.A.

5. Scientific and technical aspects of foreign development programs and foreign aid.

* Announced as members, but they subsequently refrained from formal association with the committee.

6. Technical aspects of disarmament; feasibility of detection of nuclear and missile tests.

7. Evaluation of local and global health hazards resulting from civilian and military uses of atomic energy.

8. Conservation of natural resources including strategic minerals, fossil fuels, economically useful ores; research required for development of new technologies for the future.

9. Research in medical science for the welfare of upper age groups which form an increasing fraction of the U.S. population.

10. Analyses of deficiencies in financial or facility support of research programs in the United States.

11. Make projections to forecast the impact of technology upon our society; anticipation of problems before present trends make solutions impossible.

12. Appraisal of the adequacy of the U.S. national effort in space research.

Naturally the scientists did not fully explore all of these topics but they did prepare six policy papers which the Council regarded as fundamental contributions. To illustrate the quality of the papers, one pertained to arms control and contained a proposal for the establishment of a National Peace Agency as an arm of government needed to explore the possibilities for disarmament. Its recommendations were incorporated in the only major legislation which Senator John F. Kennedy introduced in 1960; the bill was later enacted into law under his presidency. The National Peace Agency became the U.S. Arms Control and Disarmament Agency. In all fairness, I would add that proposals for such an agency had been made by Dr. David Inglis and Dr. Linus Pauling, but I must confess that, as one who worked closely with the scientists' committee, I had no knowledge then of these earlier proposals. The trick in politics is not to have ideas but to implement them. Here the perch which the scientists occupied in the political scheme of things gave them an immense advantage; they had access to political power and could be influential. Thus the proposal for a peace agency was not made in a political vacuum; Senator Kennedy was contacted directly and his aid sought in drafting his legislation.

The pioneer activities of a few scientists in 1959–1960 included

direct participation in work on the Party Platform and in assisting
Kennedy during the campaign. However, once the Democrats were
in power there was no place for a "shadow government" and the
Democratic Advisory Council was dissolved. On the Republican
side of the political fence there was no body comparable to that of
the Pollard task force. It is true that a Republican group was
formed—called the Percy Committee—but it did not number any
scientists of note among its members.

In 1964 scientists came out of political hibernation as large
numbers openly associated themselves with the Johnson-Humphrey
ticket under the banner of Scientists and Engineers for Johnson
and Humphrey. This was a bipartisan group which formed units in
major cities and conducted fund-raising and publicity drives.
Their impact was more on an organizational than on a policy-
influencing level; witness the fact that the 1964 Democratic Platform was weaker scientifically and technologically than in the
1960 version. However, the Scientists and Engineers achieved a
degree of unanimity that could be called monolithic. It was scarcely
respectable for scientists to announce themselves in favor of Senator Barry Goldwater. Admiral Lewis L. Strauss, who tried to
round up a group of eminent scientists for Goldwater, struggled
manfully but could not corral more than a brace of experts, Drs.
Edward Teller and Willard F. Libby. Dr. Teller aired his reasons
for backing Goldwater in a letter in *Science,* basing his reasons on
Goldwater's prowess with camera, ham radio, and aircraft. This
provoked a *Science* reader into responding that while it may have
qualified Goldwater to be president of the Hopi Camera Club it
did not mean he had the credentials to be the nation's chief
executive.

The 1964 entry of scientists into the hurly-burly of political life
probably made more noise than votes. But it also served to arouse
some scientists to the reality of politics; it brought home to them
the fact that as citizens they had political responsibility. A few
scientists were intrigued by politics and it will be no surprise if
they seek elective office.

The scientists and engineers could swing a total of about two million votes at the national polls. They form a minority group which has never bothered professional politicians very much, since they are not organized. Democrats take them for granted. Theoretically, if our nation were arithmetically representative of the professions, scientists should claim at least two seats in the Senate and a dozen seats in the House. So there is a deficiency of fourteen seats from the viewpoint of the scientists and engineers although I doubt if many of them ever thought of Congress in this way. Fourteen or even four good scientists could make quite a difference in Congress if they were afforded key places on committees. A single scientist on the Joint Committee on Atomic Energy might have significantly altered that group's arms bias and produced a prominent effect on nuclear policy.

Scientists are a long way from being elected to high public office but it is not impossible for them to make the transition from science to politics. If a John Glenn could succeed in Ohio politics (as he gave every indication of doing before his accident put him out of the Senate race) then I maintain that a prominent scientist like James A. Van Allen could win in Iowa. Van Allen is not about to be pried loose from his research laboratory in this decade, but I would not rule out his candidacy in the seventies should the opportunity appear. A scientist of Van Allen's stature on the Senate space committee could, in my opinion, thoroughly transform the deliberations of that body.

The 1964 election witnessed the campaigns of fifteen M.D.s, and three were elected to Congress. Doctors of medicine are thought of by scientists as representing the viewpoint of most researchers. The M.D.s who gain seats in the House of Representatives are usually of conservative stripe. They cannot be expected to exert much authority in the science-related committees on Capitol Hill. Navy Captain (ret.) William R. Anderson, former commander of the nuclear submarine *Nautilus,* ran on the Democratic ticket in Tennessee and is now a member of the House. He brings a measure of nuclear technology to Capitol Hill. The only *bona fide* Ph.D. scientist who won office in the 1964 election is Dr. Weston E. Vivian, a Canadian-born scientist who took his doctorate in 1959. Dr. Vivian later served as electronics specialist at M.I.T.'s Lincoln Laboratory. In 1960, at the age of thirty-four, Vivian helped to found the Conductron Corporation in Ann Arbor, Michigan and became vice president of the company. An expert in microwave research and missile guidance, Dr. Vivian took a flier in politics by aiming at the House seat vacated by George Meader, a long-term incumbent Republican. At long last a scientist had cracked the defenses of Congress. Time would be required for him to ascend to power, but he succeeded in being named to the House space committee.

The election of scientists to Congress had seemed to be somewhat implausible to Leo Szilard, so he hit upon a "political invention." His idea, hatched in his celestial sense of independence, was to create an organization which would solicit funds and use them to support candidates who would be inclined favorably to scientists' aims. Szilard's purpose was to create in Congress a sympathy for causes such as measures to reduce the risk of nuclear war. In June 1962 Szilard took the initiative along with other scientists in establishing a "Council for a Livable World." It made its headquarters near DuPont Circle in Washington, D.C., and proceeded to raise funds for the Council. Meanwhile, it scanned the lists of men running for office in 1962, analyzed the effect which modest sums of money might make in the campaigns of those it might favor, and directed the attention of its members to aiding these specific campaigners. For example, in 1962, a total of $58,000 was raised by way of contributions to candidates. A good share of this went to further the campaign of George McGovern, running for the Senate in South Dakota. McGovern squeaked through by a few hundred votes to become the first Democratic Senator from the state in twenty-six years. His total campaign expenses ran to about $75,000 so the Council for a Livable World could claim that it had substantially helped him.

Before the 1964 campaign began in earnest, the Council found itself embroiled in political controversy. Quentin N. Burdick, North Dakota lawyer and son of the long-term Republican Congressman Usher Burdick, had been given some $14,000 in financial aid through the Council. In the spring of 1964 the favored North Dakotan suddenly started mailing checks back to their senders. The reason for this abrupt U-turn was that he had been confronted with the rantings of a right-wing columnist who pictured Szilard as a wild-eyed radical in favor of unilateral disarmament. Szilard never lived to see this issue thrashed out. He died in his sleep in early summer and was given a midsummer posthumous "tribute" by a group of Republican Senators, who ganged up on the nuclear scientists and their Council in a lengthy Senate colloquy aimed at discrediting the organization. The prime Senate time allocated to Szilard really meant that Szilard's political invention had been effective.

The Council for a Livable World supported eighteen candidates in the course of the 1964 campaigns. It urged priority support to five candidates who faced strong right-wing opposition: *For the Senate:* Representative Ralph R. Harding (D. Idaho); Senator Gale W. McGee (D. Wyo.); Senator Frank E. Moss (D. Utah); Representative Joseph M. Montoya (D. N.M.); Senator Edmund S. Muskie (D. Maine). All but Ralph R. Harding were elected to the Senate.

The Council gave late campaign support to: Senator Philip A. Hart (D. Mich.); Joseph D. Tydings (D. Md.); Senator Ralph Yarborough (D. Tex.). All three candidates won handily; in addition, the Council recommended Senators Albert Gore (D. Tenn.) and Eugene J. McCarthy (D. Minn.) for re-election and both were returned to the Senate.

In races for House seats the Council's candidates included: Representative John V. Lindsay (R. N.Y.); Representative Seymour Halpern (R. N.Y.); Charles B. Officer (D. N.H.); Jerry L. Pettis (R. Cal.); Representative Abner W. Sibal (R. Conn.); Representative Stanley R. Tupper (R. Maine); Weston E. Vivian (D. Mich.). In these races Sibal, Pettis and Officer lost, the last-named by a margin small enough to require a recount. The Council's score card at the end of 1964 read: 14 winners—4 losers. It spent or got its members to make individual contributions totaling $102,000;

almost all the funds were directed to states in which campaign expenditures are not normally very high.

It is apparent both from the Council's activities and the foregoing descriptions of scientists engaged in political work that politics will feel an even greater impact from scientists in the future. A breed of scientist-politician is emerging in the United States—a strange political animal which is apt to be regarded with some dismay by the professional politician. Long accustomed to the manipulation of power, the latter may fear this newcomer who has his own cult of power and now unites with his. Uncomfortable as the conventional politician may be with the new technology, he may look wistfully back to the days when he was king and the atom was an intellectual curiosity.

SCIENTISTS
AND
10 THE EXECUTIVE

If the author's thesis that the Congress is in a supine position with respect to the onrush of science and technology is accepted, then it becomes clear that the real decision-making takes place elsewhere in government. The location of the center of gravity on R & D decision-making was mainly in the Pentagon before Sputnik. After the Soviet success in 1957 more and more of the decisions involving research and development centered in the White House. President Eisenhower formalized a science advisory mechanism which has since expanded into a weighty apparatus in the Executive Office. Thus scientists have played a greater advisory role in decisions affecting the nation's welfare, although on some issues their advice has been disregarded.

The determinative postwar factor in the evolution of U.S. research and development was the Cold War. The nation's concern for its security and the potential of modern technology caused most of the total R & D funds to be dedicated to defense. For example, in the first post-Sputnik budget, the total federal outlays for nonsecurity research and development amounted to less than one-eighth of the $7.1 billion. One might quibble over whether NASA funds were primarily to reassure the U.S. sense of security; I would resolve the issue by describing this as money spent for "flag science." Although many legislators voted for NASA funds thinking

Defense Department	$5,237 million
Atomic Energy Commission	925
National Aeronautics and Space Administration	300
Health, Education, and Welfare	279
Agriculture	139
National Science Foundation	69
Interior Department	68
Commerce	30
All other	75
	$7,122 million
	(i.e., 7.122 billions)

that they would bear military rewards, it became evident that space was to be an area of status-seeking.

The above budget then describes the profile of U.S. research and development as funded by federal agencies shortly after the scientists ascended to advisory power in the White House. It is provocative to jump ahead to the 1966 fiscal budget and note how the profile has been altered in a span of seven years. In this way we may observe the gross changes in federal spending which surely point to policy changes, leaving aside for the moment the influence of science advice. The new order of federal R & D spending is:

Department of Defense	$ 6,875.3 million
National Aeronautics and Space Administration	5,100.0
Atomic Energy Commission	1,292.2
Health, Education, and Welfare	942.0
National Science Foundation	266.0
Agriculture	256.0
Interior	129.0
Commerce	68.1
All other	211.4
Total (including additional facilities)	$15,444.2 million

The most prominent feature of this budget, apart from its total, is the NASA appropriation. As already explained, this budget item was primarily a Presidential innovation and cannot be ascribed to a consensus of White House science advisers. Without the federal outlay for space the total would have been about $10 billion, which would represent less than a doubling in seven years. This rate of spending actually represents a slowdown as compared with earlier years when the doubling time was roughly four years. As we have seen, this paring back of R & D appropriations coincided with closer congressional scrutiny of research; the size of R & D funds clearly caused Congressmen to begin assessing science and technology in the light of other expenditures.

On the face of it, the two most obvious features of the R & D budget after scientists trooped to the White House to act in advisory roles were contradictions—a space program not of their choosing and a cutback in R & D expansion. But the stark statistics conceal the innumerable tugging and pulling of forces operating at many levels within the officialdom of government. For example, R & D defense expenditures are down for fiscal year 1966 as compared to preceding years. This reflects not just a thaw in the Cold War but a change in philosophy of the Defense Department in which key scientists were highly influential, both within government and without. The sufficiency and redundancy of strategic weapons systems allowed for cutbacks.

Probably this comparison of the federal R & D budget profile is too harsh a criterion to apply to the influence of scientists at the White House level. As the latest added ingredient of policy-making, science advice will probably take longer to evaluate and it may manifest itself in subtler ways than by showing up as budgetary changes. Nonetheless, the most effective means of control of R & D is at the budgetary level; it is here that decision-making is of a guillotine nature. Science advisers may give lofty advice and complex recommendations, but in the end the Bureau of the Budget must convert the words into deeds—into approval or disapproval of project or program funds requested by a government agency.

Evaluation of the effectiveness of the White House science advisers is difficult because of the low visibility of the work of the various individuals and groups attached to the Executive Office in an advisory capacity. For example, the White House does not issue any annual report on the status of science and technology. Presidential advisers are very discreet in exposing controversial R & D issues to the view of outsiders. Task force reports are rarely published; even the names of consultants are held confidential. Further-more, the President's science adviser serves a relatively short term of office and each one has his own method of dealing with prob-lems. Since the White House represents a Grand Junction where the pathways of political power intersect, it is difficult to separate out the causative factors in decisions made by the President on matters scientific or technical.

Then, too, the advice-taker must be considered as preponderantly more significant at the White House level than the purveyor of recommendations. The President may or may not take to heart scientific advice. He may find the scientists' jargon and syntax alien to his own as President Truman did when he was briefed in the late summer of 1949 on Joe I, the first Soviet nuclear test. A special group of eminent scientists transmitted and tried to translate the pertinent detection data to the President but there was a real gap between the parties. When Mr. Truman left office he expressed himself publicly as doubting the validity of the Soviet test. This was bewildering to scientists who examined the data and knew that it constituted proof of the Soviet nuclear bomb.

There is no need to detail the pre-Sputnik arrangements for injecting R & D advice into the Executive Office. Vannevar Bush's relations to Roosevelt were of an *ad hoc* nature. Truman had Dr. John R. Steelman, the economist-sociologist, as a White House counselor but he was not regarded as a powerhouse for science. Korea served to hoist some warning flags that science might need more high-level attention and Truman established a Science Ad-visory Committee in 1951 under the Office of Defense Mobiliza-tion. But he had no official science adviser and no eminent scientist could claim a close relationship to him. Science was still not yet within the orbit of Presidential power.

It was during Eisenhower's second term that the shock wave of scientific events crashed down upon the White House and pro-duced visible changes in the science advisory system there. A very large segment of the scientific community felt that a shake-up was long overdue and they welcomed the impact of Sputnik upon political affairs. Many scientists deeply resented the Eisenhower regime's blindness to the affairs of science which were discolored by security excesses, the Oppenheimer disgrace, the fallout scandal, the nuclear test issue, and a lack of sympathy for intellectualism. Although funds for R & D increased sharply under Eisenhower, they were aimed in the direction of a weapons culture, and the climate for science itself was chill.

The Soviet success with ballistic missiles shocked the American people and politicians who had lulled themselves into a reverie that the United States was the chosen land for scientific accomplishments. Although President Eisenhower personally downgraded the significance of Soviet technological triumphs, he was forced to give ground. In a nationwide television address on November 7, 1957, on the heels of Sputnik II and a wave of publicity over the orbiting of Laika, a dog, the President revealed:

> . . . I have created the office of Special Assistant to the President for Science and Technology. This man, who will be aided by a staff of scientists and a strong advisory group of outstanding experts reporting to him and to me, will have the active responsibility of helping me follow through on the program of scientific improvement of our defenses.

It is significant that this new office was oriented along defense needs. James R. Killian, president of the Massachusetts Institute of Technology, was named as Eisenhower's science adviser. Not a scientist himself, Killian brought to the post a thorough knowledge of federal bureaucracy and a wide acquaintance with scientists and technologists.

The scientific experts mentioned by Eisenhower were organized in the President's Science Advisory Committee (PSAC) and they were headed by Killian. The committee included on its initial roster the following: Robert F. Bacher, physics professor, California Institute of Technology; William O. Baker, vice president, Bell Telephone Laboratories; Lloyd V. Berkner, president, Associated Universities; Hans A. Bethe, physics professor, Cornell University;

Detlev W. Bronk, president, National Academy of Sciences; James H. Doolittle, Lt. Gen., vice president, Shell Oil Company; James B. Fisk, vice president, Bell Telephone Laboratories; Caryl P. Haskins, president, Carnegie Institution of Washington; George B. Kistiakowsky, chemistry professor, Harvard University; Edwin H. Land, president, Polaroid Corporation; Edward M. Purcell, physics professor, Harvard University; Isidor I. Rabi, physics professor, Columbia University; H. P. Robertson, physics professor, California Institute of Technology; Jerome B. Wiesner, director, Electronics Research Laboratory, M.I.T.; Jerrold R. Zacharias, physics professor, Massachusetts Institute of Technology; Herbert York, chief scientist, Department of Defense.

About half of the members could be called active in research and two-thirds confined their specialization to the physical sciences. Scientists on the PSAC task force generally represented two geographic areas, northeastern United States, especially Boston, and California.

It will be recalled that President Eisenhower suffered a stroke in November, 1957. By February 4, 1958, he had recovered sufficiently to honor scientists at a White House dinner party. Some forty-nine couples, including many high-ranking officers, were feted to a white-tie-and-tails dinner which displayed gold service at the table and four wines with appropriate courses. The scientists had assumed new social status, but it remained to be seen how they would fare as advice-givers and decision-makers.

Killian and his cohorts faced a wide variety of problems in 1958—priority items in defense, a space program, educational demands for the future supply of scientists and engineers, "ugly ducklings" like the nuclear airplane and the nuclear rocket, coordination of federal R & D, fallout, and nuclear test policy. The latter, as has been discussed earlier, was an issue on which some committee members focused to bring about a reversal in U.S. policy. Unfortunately, the PSAC group suffered from the faults of a high-level advisory body. It could air the problem and make recommendations but it had no operating function. It was organized too late to encourage the research which could have swung the balance in favor of an effective test-detection system in 1958 when the Geneva talks were critical.

The PSAC experts soon discovered that politics was much more influential in government policy than physics. They found that they could reach general agreement, for example, on the matter of canceling the ANP project (Aircraft Nuclear Propulsion), but this was technical advice which was hard for a politician to swallow when the Joint Committee on Atomic Energy fought for its pet. For years Joint Committeemen like Senator Jackson and Congressman Mel Price had been gifted with a vision that saw ANP flying in a year or so; they seemed to have special intelligence of a competitive Soviet nuclear bomber. In the collision of science and politics over such an issue as ANP the obvious tactic for the President was to stall. Finally under President Kennedy the atomic airplane was canceled, but not before a billion dollars had been spent.

How political should a PSAC scientist be? Should he give advice on the basis of how he interprets "the national good"? Should he take an academic view of a technical problem or should he season this with a sense of political reality? It would seem that the name of the President's committee identifies the primary qualification of its members as scientific experts. Since they serve an advisory capacity, their environment can produce an awareness of political factors. The latter is easily imparted by good staff liaison work or by the simple fact that almost every PSAC member had a background of experience in dealing with bureaucracy. The President has his own political advisers and it would appear that the prime function of the PSAC group would be to give advice on scientific and technical merit of various projects, proposals, and programs. The presence on the PSAC group of members like Detlev Bronk and Jerome Wiesner injected more than a few grains of political salt into the committee's deliberations.

The preponderance of physical scientists on PSAC raised the question of how representative it was of American science. Was not the committee overweighted against, say, the field of biological science? But this was not the basic question. Even if all the sciences were to be allocated membership on PSAC by some numerical relationship, there would still remain the same question which has been raised with regard to the National Academy of Sciences. How could PSAC claim to be representative of U.S. science?

The PSAC problem was even more vexing than that posed for the Academy because the latter had a multitude of committees and advisory groups and could be reckoned as more representative than a single eighteen-man committee. If we look upon PSAC as a potent priesthood of science, we may inquire into the means by which PSAC divines what the general assembly of U.S. scientists thinks about the state of science. The PSAC members are extremely stuffy about discussing their committee deliberations; I have had difficulty finding any scientists who have been solicited for an opinion by PSAC members. The committee holds eleven two-day sessions each year but only occasionally does the outside world learn what transpires in PSAC. Usually this communication takes the form of a published report of a task force, but these are few and far between. The first such was a brief report, "Introduction to Outer Space," dated March 28, 1958, which was fairly colorless as a policy statement but did contain one warning: "It would not be in the national interest to exploit space science at the cost of weakening our efforts in other scientific endeavors. This need not happen if we plan our national program for space science and technology as part of a balanced effort in all science and technology." Can one inspect the current R & D budget and find evidence of the balance which PSAC recommended? In fact, what kind of over-all balanced program did PSAC have in mind? There is no published record of any PSAC recommendation for such a program.

If the President's committee were to publish a recommended program for a balanced effort in the nation's research and development, then the scientists outside the White House could function in a democratic manner by individually appraising the programs and feeding back reflections on them to PSAC members, to scientists in government, and to Congressmen. There would be the possibility of discussing the issue in the nation's news forums and within scientific societies. Granting that the scientific community has no internal cohesion or mechanism for acting as a collective Solomon on the matter, it could nonetheless function in a diffuse democratic manner. Furthermore, competent individuals within our society would then be in a position to translate the technical issues into popular terms and thus to facilitate a more general discussion. In this way society at large would become acquainted with the goals and aspirations of science.

President Kennedy touched upon this matter when he said: "The question in all our minds today is how science can best continue its service to the nation, to the people, to the world, in the years to come." It would seem that a basic first step should be definition and promulgation of the issues. This is perhaps not PSAC's responsibility, but somewhere in the White House, presumably in the office of the President's science adviser, the challenge should be faced squarely. An annual report titled *The State of Science and Its Prospects for Society* could serve as an excellent vehicle for exposing issues to public appreciation.

PSAC brings up the "national interest" and long-range policy for research in connection with its recommendations on high-energy physics. As expressed by Dr. Donald F. Hornig, chairman of PSAC under President Johnson: "It is in the national interest to support vigorous advancement of high-energy physics as a fundamental field of science." This is a determination of a group of scientists, but how does society react to such a specification? As we have noted, Congress has wearied of the excessive fiscal demands of high-energy physics and shows a preference for projects which have more meaning for voters. Dr. Hornig recognized the problem, for he said: ". . . if science is influenced by the democratic political process, if considerations other than scientific merit enter into our choices and decisions, it is up to the scientists to make clear to the layman what the bases for choice are, and what they understand by merit in basic research. In short, we must communicate a wider sense of the meaning of scientific research, its internal value system, and its value to the nation and its people." This advice is well taken but the formula for successful dialogue is not revealed.

President Eisenhower's first science adviser, Killian, had his hands full trying to relate PSAC and himself to the pressing issues which reached the White House from the operating agencies of government. In attempting to put the federal R & D house in order, Killian saw a need for some coordinating body which would resolve squabbles among the various agencies and buffer PSAC against a flood of unwanted business. To this end an Executive Order was issued creating the Federal Council for Science and Technology (FCST). This Council is essentially a subcabinet composed of policy-makers from eight major government departments and agencies; it is both a clearing house and a lower tribunal for adjudicating the conflicts of the thirty-eight agencies which claim a chunk or a sliver of the R & D pie. The President's science adviser presides over FCST, and its work is divided among the following committees:

A. Standing Committee
   a. Panel of scientific personnel
   b. Panel on methods for improving federally financed research
   c. Panel on laboratory astrophysics
B. International Committee
C. Committee on Long-Range Planning
D. Interagency Committee on Oceanography
E. Interdepartmental Committee for Atmospheric Sciences
F. Coordinating Committee on Materials Research and Development
G. Technical Committee on High Energy Physics
H. Committee on Natural Resources
I. Committee on Science Information
J. Committee on Water Resources Research

Problems unresolved by the Council or by the science adviser may be passed on to PSAC as the higher tribunal, but not necessarily the court of last resort. While issues get debated in committee, they are also handled by the interested agencies in devious ways. For example, enthusiasts anxious to promote an agency project may leak stories to the press in order to whip up public support or solicit aid from Capitol Hill. The problem of establishing the proper liaison between the White House and congressional R & D committees was a factor in the creation of the Office of Science and Technology (OST) under the direction of the President's science adviser. The OST was established June 8, 1962, and its first director was Dr. Jerome B. Wiesner, President Kennedy's science adviser. Thus Dr. Wiesner was the first adviser to wear four hats —one as the President's adviser, one as chairman of PSAC, another as chairman of FCST, and a fourth as director of OST. In addition to these roles, Dr. Wiesner operated as adviser to the Bureau of the Budget. For his many activities Wiesner needed a staff and this was provided in OST where he chose eleven men to cover various fields of science and technology. He realized that the committee structure of PSAC and FCST was cumbersome. A committee is like a car without wheels; it will not go anywhere under its own power. It needs staff work, especially if the committee experts meet only occasionally for a day or two.

The PSAC-FCST-OST trinity gave the President's science adviser great power within the federal structure of science and technology, so much so that some Washingtonians muttered that he had become a science czar. Whether or not the noun had relevance, officials in the federal agencies knew that power in R & D matters had been congealed in the White House. Few would deny that this was now the seat of power. But the use of power was of low political visibility; both those within and without government were often in the dark about who really made decisions on R & D matters and how the process worked. The White House science affairs involved consultantships with some three hundred specialists, but the roster of these men was held confidential by the Office of Science and Technology. An air of secrecy often surrounded the activities of the science advisory staff.

I was reminded of the parallel to Vannevar Bush's Research and Development Board (RDB) which had been his brainchild for directing military R & D in the early postwar years. Top-level committees populated by "weekend consultants" attempted to deal with the Pentagon's research and development programs, but the gap between the laboratory and the committees of RDB was too great. Furthermore, the military found ways to infiltrate RDB and to outmaneuver the Board. It was just not possible to make this committee system of R & D control work when the actual work was done in widely scattered laboratories. Thus RDB turned out to be a depressant instead of a stimulant to creative research in the Defense Department.

Imperfections in the White House science advisory mechanism will not, I believe, be resolved by patching up the present organization. Some of the defects are organic and go deep within the present makeshift structure. There is the very real question as to whether any group of part-time science advisers or full-time lower-echelon assistants can piece together a wise national program in a privileged sanctuary isolated from contact with the public. As one reads the testimony of Wiesner, there is clear admission of the need for a vigorous interplay of the inner sanctum and the outer world, but he implies that this takes place adequately through liaison with Congress. Testifying before the House Select Committee on Government Research, Wiesner said:

Our attempts to understand these changing patterns [of science and their impact on society] require the utmost effort and cooperation of both the expert, who can illuminate the choices and help to plot the right paths, and the layman, who in his own community and through his representatives must determine these overall objectives and their value. That is why the interest of the Congress in these areas is particularly welcome at this time. Your appreciation of the full dimensions and capabilities of our national involvement in science and technology will enhance the nation's ability to allocate its scientific and technical resources in ways that best serve national purposes.

Since the average Congressman serves as middleman between expert and layman, this double communication from expert to Congressman to layman is a dubious relay operation.

From what has gone before, it appears that the limited exposure of White House science advice to the general public places a maximum reliance upon the good sense and qualifications of the new elite. When the few decide what is good for the many, government is shaken to its democratic roots. But our society is confronted with the enigma that only a relatively few are highly specialized and they talk in a strange tongue. The public is thus forced to back science on the basis of blind faith. It really has little choice and is so isolated from decision-making that it does not know that it has a choice.

Recent interchanges between scientists have highlighted the fact that scientists disagree on what is good for science, so there is apt to be even more disharmony over what is good for society. Confining the matter to the area of fundamental science, we find that scientists are confronted with the necessity for making decisions on science policy. Dr. Alvin Weinberg phrased the problem as follows:

> As science grows, its demands on our society's resources grow. It seems inevitable that science's demands will eventually be limited by what society can allocate to it. We shall then have to make choices. These choices are of two kinds. We shall have to choose among different, often incommensurable, fields of science—between, for example, high-energy physics and oceanography or between molecular biology and science of metals. We shall also have to choose among the different institutions that receive support for science from the government— among universities, governmental laboratories and industry.

Weinberg was critical of the White House machinery for making these choices; he went to the heart of the matter and focused on the criteria for making policy decisions. He defined three criteria: scientific, technological, and social merit.

In the area of science, the postwar upsurge of research spending has been so prodigious that demand has outrun the supply of federal dollars. Thus the President's Science Advisory Committee has had to make decisions—or recommendations which are often tantamount to decisions—which alter the flow of federal funds to the various fields of basic science. For quite a number of years the gush of government money did not reach any critical mark in the reservoir of science and few outcries were heard from scientists. But when Congress decided to squeeze back on federal support, rifts began to appear in the domain of science. Weinberg proposed that the criterion of scientific merit be the extent to which a field of science contributes to its bordering areas. In other words, a field which contained within itself the fruits of its research would merit less support than one which scattered fertile seeds to neighboring areas. This criterion, although wise in its formulation, is not easy to implement. It involves advance information on experiments or at least prejudgment of their outcome. On this basis no government dollars would flow to really radical ideas or to "way-out" scientists like Albert Einstein. One would need a committee of Einsteins which would probably admit that it could not give any worthwhile advice.

It strikes me that it is absurd even to attempt to mastermind science by a top-echelon committee at the White House level. The existing science advisory structure is already top-heavy and too far removed from the creative zones of research. Science has grown so rapidly that the government has responded by patching up its administrative structure rather than by attempting any basic reforms. The fundamental goals of expanding human knowledge and capitalizing on creativity through research can be realized most effectively if the centers of scientific research are kept as free and as healthy as possible. The whole purpose of pumping over $2 billion each year into the body of basic science is to ensure that our country preserve its vitality and never falter in fostering innovation on a wide front. As Norbert Wiener summed up shortly before his death:

The purpose of science in society is to enable us to react homeostatically to the vicissitudes of the future. This future is, however, not one which we can completely foresee beyond a certain very limited point, which moves ahead in time as our experience moves ahead. This being the case, we must always possess a much larger stock of information concerning the environment, physical, medical and social, than we shall probably use in any particular course of history. It is of the utmost importance to our safety against the vicissitudes of the future that this stock of fundamental scientific information be kept extremely wide.

On this view, the United States pays out its money for basic research as an insurance premium. Most scientists are in agreement that the university environment is most favorable to the flourishing of basic research. The federal government recognizes this fact and it has not been stingy in its support of research on campus. But because of the many agencies handing out funds, the large universities face a veritable blizzard of paperwork for the many separate projects which are funded by separate agencies, each of which demands its own accounting and often makes laboratories into private empires which are wasteful and inefficient.

If the government trusts the individual colleges, institutes, and universities to do basic research, it would seem appropriate for the government to trust them to decide how funds might be allocated most wisely. Rather than have a large university's research effort multisected by conflicting contractual lines, it would be better to have lump-sum awards to the university and allow that institution to decide how the research funds should be split up. Such a proposal is not apt to warm the cardiac cockles of many a university president who would far rather have somebody off-campus make the research decisions, but it would bring the decision-making close to the core of creativity. Furthermore, it would inhibit the untoward growth of campus empires which produce a distorted research program. At the same time one can slice off a big section of bureaucratic fat that has bulged around the midriff of federal agencies concerned with administering research contracts. It would diminish the wheeling and dealing of scientist-promoters who have won large R & D contracts through their Washington contacts.

Since such lump-sum support of research would bypass the separate government agencies, I believe that the awards ought to be made from a single central source. A logical agency for such activity would be a Department of Science whose head would be of cabinet rank. He would make funds available to educational institutions on a formula which would encourage participation by the various states. For example, half of the funds might be outright grants and half might be awarded on the basis of matching funds supplied by the state. A single uniform method of accounting would be adopted by the Department of Science, thus cutting through the maze of record-keeping and contractual red tape of the present agencies.

An advantage of concentrating responsibility for basic research in one Department of Science would be that the Secretary would be politically visible and accountable to the public. The over-all research program of the United States would be a matter of public record, for the Secretary would be required to make a comprehensive annual report on the state of science in the nation. No such accounting is now made to the American public nor does one appear to be entertained by the science advisory setup in the White House. One could see, for example, the balance between research done by lump-sum awards to educational institutions and that done within the framework of the government agencies, both within federal laboratories such as the National Bureau of Standards and in places like the Brookhaven National Laboratory.

The new Department of Science would have responsibility for all basic research carried out within the government. Actually it was not until 1964 that a high-level study group began to appreciate how many research laboratories were in existence throughout the government. It discovered that there were approximately 150 (the exact number was in doubt) laboratories owned or operated by the government. Little real interrelation of these research centers was in evidence; often some maintained an attitude of stern detachment, presumably to protect their own empires from invasion. Freedom of research is one thing, but completely self-willed activity without respect for work done elsewhere is quite a different matter. Such duplication of effort is minimized in university-based research by openness of publication and by ease of access to visitors. Isolated research laboratories such as those maintained by the Defense Department are more prone to duplication because of restricted publication and intercourse with the outside world.

Since the new Department would coordinate basic research and determine in-house priorities for its various programs, it could well absorb the functions of the Federal Council for Science and Technology (at least the research phase of FCST's role) of the President's Science Advisory Committee and of much of the Office of Science and Technology. There would be no need for a special assistant for Science and Technology since this function would be served by the Secretary of Science.

A number of illustrious scientists have opposed centralization of research within government during the course of years when a Department of Science and Technology has been debated. Dr. Roger Revelle, an outstanding oceanographer, put forth the view that "the last thing we need is a Department of Science hovering over all like the Archangel Gabriel. Science permeates—or should permeate—our entire federal structure and should not be concentrated in a single department." I would agree with Revelle if such concentration meant amassing all scientific resources into a single Pentagon of Science, a regimented bastion of tightly controlled research. But most of the scientists' objections to a Department of Science and Technology really pertains to the nine-tenths of the R & D activity which is not basic research. The proposal advanced here is that the nine-tenths remain in a status quo pending further examination of its structure.

Under the new establishment for science, research would be carried out largely in the same sites as now although some consolidation might be effected. In the field of atomic research it is now apparent that some more drastic reform is necessary because the military R & D function of the Atomic Energy Commission is basically fulfilled. Huge production facilities weigh down the AEC and some should now be mothballed while the remainder are turned over to the Defense Department. The Department of Science would take over the civilian research functions of the AEC and rehabilitate the field of nuclear research. The Oak Ridge National Laboratory, for example, needs to be reoriented along new lines, perhaps of a biological nature. In general there appears to be a strategic shift in the offing which will place emphasis upon the biological sciences. This reflects both the need and the opportunity. Of the total research funds spent by the United States only a small fraction goes to bettering man's personal condition—toward freeing him from the burden of ancient bodily afflictions. For example, it is now estimated that one of every five Americans born today will incur an incidence of cancer. The opportunity exists for making very impressive inroads on the toll caused by disease because of three circumstances:

First, the success of modern research and development in fulfilling national security needs allows scientific manpower and resources to be dedicated to new areas. The shift from physical to biological research fits in with this turning point in U.S. research. This point will be treated in more detail in the next chapter.

Second, the great reservoir of new knowledge and techniques accumulated in the past decade largely in the area of physical research is ready to spill its riches into the bordering field of biological science.

Third, the field of biology itself is ripe for exploitation. Breakthroughs in biological knowledge have been scored at the molecular level of organization of the human cell.

The new Department of Science would serve to bring fresh approaches to research, including the possibility of the massive shift in emphasis from physical to biological science. However, this would not be done at the expense of physical research. The latter will continue to nourish contiguous areas of science and will need full fiscal sustenance.

Establishment of the new Department would require legislative action, since it would specifically abolish the present Atomic Energy Commission. It would also do away with the present National Science Foundation, transferring some of its personnel and functions to the single Department of Science. The NSF has not been a howling success by any means and it has shown an inability to deal with large-scale projects, such as Project Mohole for investigating the structure of the earth's crust through ocean-based deep drilling. Incorporating NSF's planning and support functions within the Department of Science will allow for orderly growth of pilot projects to large scale through employment of facilities like those formerly under the direction of the AEC. The Office of Naval Research, which is now on the downgrade, would be merged with the new science agency as would the Office of Saline Water now under the Interior Department. The newly expanded National Bureau of Standards and the Weather Bureau would also be consolidated under the management of the single science agency. Many of these old-line bureaus have only marginal relation to their present agency management and a realignment of their administration is long overdue.

The activities of these various research centers and bureaus are jealously watched over by a score of congressional groups, most of which will be reluctant to release their reins of power. However, a concerted drive by the Administration, backed up by a solid reorganization plan for scientific research and reinforced by data to show how operating costs may be reduced, would be difficult for Congress to buck. Scientific projects and research facilities have grown like Topsy since the war and it would be most startling if the administrative arrangements now in practice were really efficient or appropriate. The National Science Foundation which was set up in 1950 was supposed to develop a national science policy but its timid leadership shied away from anything so adventurous; it did not even manage to take an inventory of U.S. research facilities, much less get around to doing something about reorganizing science in government.

If the Administration reforms its R & D structure, then as a consequence Congress would be obliged to conform. Rather than have a score of committees, subcommittees, and panels overseeing research activities, it could compress this gallimaufry into a single Senate and a single House Committee on Research. This by itself would represent a great improvement in the present arrangement which is akin to a jumble of a dozen jigsaw puzzles taken from as many separate boxes. As a result Congress never sees a single integrated picture but only bits and pieces of parts of the over-all research business of the United States. Under such a condition it is whimsical to talk of introducing balance into the research program—or even to speak of a national program as such.

The social impact of modern research is too explosive for a nation to proceed blindly and cavalierly in such activity without making an effort to sense how new developments may affect society.

This is an area which the National Science Foundation might have been expected to explore but, again, timidity at the top steered clear of such studies. In 1964 the government gave some indication of its awareness of the need to appreciate technological change when it created a National Commission on Technology, Automation and Economic Progress, but this is a far cry from incorporating planning activities within the substance of a government agency. I would propose that the Department of Science establish a Division of Social Impact so that concurrent study would push forward on the societal significance of contemporary research. Such planning could act as a sort of early warning system to appraise well in advance the potential repercussions of modern scientific developments. Many discoveries and inventions profoundly affect the character of the nation's economy and its requirement for skilled labor. A single development like the transistor can mushroom within a few years from a concept into a complex of industries. The evolution of what the author calls a Ph.D.-based economy carries with it far-reaching consequences for our educational programs, for the economic vitality of individual communities and states, and for the status of the United States in a world that is increasingly conscious of technological prestige.

No mention can be made of the impact of science on society without discussing the negative values which modern technology may entail if there is no advance accommodation to it. For example, agricultural productivity is boosted by the use of hundreds of different insecticides. But this potent brand of chemical warfare directed at pests may backfire upon its user in ways that are not immediately obvious. Here careful attention must be given to the contamination of the biosphere—that thin rim of earth, air, and water upon which all life is founded. The possibilities of ecological upset are infinite, and a careless tinkering with one niche of nature may ricochet in oblique modes and show up in unexpected places and with nasty consequences. Here the government should show an advance concern that is self-policing so that it becomes unnecessary for a Rachel Carson to sound alarm. A responsible government tuned to the nature of modern technology should not have to be jolted by external criticism into an awareness of environmental hazards. As we have demonstrated in the case of radioactive fallout, the United States pursued a stubborn policy of avoiding facts, much to its detriment in the court of world opinion.

Science and foreign policy are often intimately interlinked. Scientists recognized this truism in the fifties and attempted to persuade the U.S. Department of State to take science seriously. Preliminary efforts to reform the State Department's old ways toward science were unsuccessful. To cite a single example where an ounce of foresight might have paid off in tons of reward, we may mention the matter of seismology and the Nuclear Test Ban Treaty. As detailed in previous pages, the Test Ban Treaty was in the air early in 1954 when radioactive fallout from U.S. nuclear tests produced widespread fear. Yet when the experts met at Geneva to discuss a system for monitoring explosions, they lacked basic data on seismic detection of underground explosions and earthquakes. Neither the Defense Department nor the AEC did the relatively simple homework which might have saved the day at Geneva in 1958. Needless to say the National Science Foundation did not have the courage or foresight to fund a $50,000 or $100,000 research project which could have turned up all-important data. No genius was required to foresee that these data would be needed. Benjamin Franklin's maxims about the "want of a nail" and "a little neglect may breed mischief" take on a much more important connotation in an age of computers, ICBMs, and H-bombs.

"Every time you scientists make a major invention," President Kennedy said in a speech to a distinguished conference of scientists, "we politicians have to make a new invention to cope with it." Too often the political "inventions" are delayed until the produce of science turns ugly and even foul. Then the decisions which have to be made often involve political trauma and fiscal pain. It should not be beyond the wit of man to extract sweet honey from the hive of science without attracting a swarm of retaliation.

THE TYRANNY

OF

11 TECHNOLOGY

Assuming that the proper connective links can be established between expert and layman, the layman will inevitably ask questions which will challenge the specialist's ability to peer into the technological future. What kind of over-the-horizon vision do scientists have? Can they foresee the sudden discontinuities which represent singular breakthroughs in their fields? Scientists claim no special sense of clairvoyance, nor is there any inner arrow of science which directs it upon a course inherently favorable to useful discoveries. But because scientists are the custodians of their specialties, and because these are so little understood by the public, there is a natural tendency for the experts to be queried about the future. And because the public looks upon scientists as precise in their disciplines it often expects naïvely that they are foreordained with prescience.

A sociologist with nothing else to do once compiled an inventory of scientists' predictions and subjected them to the acid test of history. Result: he gave the physicists and chemists a very low score as prophets. But when I examined the framework of his "analysis" I found it so flimsy as to reflect more on the critic than on the so-called seers. If you take a group of physicists and ask them (as we have seen was done randomly after the war): "When will Russia have the A-bomb?" you get a variety of answers. The more famous the scientist the greater is the tendency to single out his guess and hold it up to examination. Make no mistake about it, scientists are human and if asked a question they will give some kind of answer, if only to get rid of the questioner or to pontificate, as all men do at times. The specialist is apt to be too close to his field and to see too vividly all the obstacles. The men to ask when Russia might get its first bomb should have been those with knowledge of the Russian economy, for it was the state of Soviet industry which determined when it would operate its atomic production plants. In the case of an American physicist making an estimate of when the Soviets might have their first nuclear weapon, he would have in his mind at the time a great many assumptions. These obviously would never appear in print; the answer was a concrete date, say 1951 or 1961 or, if one was lucky, 1949. The fact is that such estimation was, early in the game, a kind of open-ended guessing. No one—*not even the Soviets*—really knew in 1946 when the Soviets would test their first A-bomb. Much depended upon how quickly various separate projects and industrial efforts would merge into a single final product.

Very often I have been asked, especially after delivering a public lecture, whether there would be a nuclear war *and when*. This is a question that I have steadfastly refused to answer, since there is little upon which to base an answer unless it be one's intrinsic pessimism or optimism. But some people are on record as making positive predictions, such as, *It is a certainty that there will be nuclear war within ten years.* Now there is a *certain* probability that nuclear war will erupt on the planet within a decade, but this is not 100 percent. To assume that scientists are close to knowing the percentage is to believe them to be oracles.

Science is the substratum upon which today's technology is built. The public normally is aware of the technology not the science. It is the technology which is expensive and which has the greatest impact upon our society. Roughly nine-tenths of R & D costs are associated with technology or with what scientists call "hardware" —that which is visible to the public eye or which can be appreciated in terms of products or techniques that have social significance.

While the really impressive developments in science defy forecast, technological events lend themselves more readily to prediction although their time scale may still be ambiguous. The injection into orbit of an earth-circling device was such an event. It was no unforeseen miracle even though many were astonished by the audacity of the Soviets in beating the United States into space. The debut of the world's first artificial satellite was not fixed in time by any scientific breakthrough; it was determined by the marshaling of technological skills and resources. This was an effort to which a time scale could be assigned based upon the engineering programs needed to fashion a rocket and equip it with a power plant sufficiently powerful to lift it off the earth's surface. It was an exercise in weight-lifting by means of sophisticated engineering based on laws of physics well known to Newton. Einstein was a prerequisite for the A-bomb, but the Space Age had its foundations buried in three centuries of science. In fact, ballistics is founded on the works of Galileo, and the rocket traces back to the eleventh century and the Chinese *huo chien,* a fire arrow propelled by slow-burning powder.

Society is today nearing the two-thirds landmark of the twentieth century and from this vantage point we can gain some perspective on the accelerating trend of technology and its impact upon society. We may also peer into the future, always mindful that the "main events" in modern technology are not easy to foresee. Nonetheless, there are plenty of signs to indicate that society is being pummeled by the ever mounting intensity of technological forces. The assault began fairly slowly, actually in England toward the end of the eighteenth century when James Watt, an instrument-maker and engineer, turned his inventive talent to the modification of a crude steam engine developed by an ironmonger, Thomas Newcomen. The latter had made a piston-type engine run by steam to pump water from coal mines. Watt converted this into a practical engine, and subsequent improvements resulted in the application of the steam engine to propulsion of boats and trains.

With the emergence of steam as a substitute for animal or water

power, factories sprang up in England, especially as cotton-spin-
ning was adapted to machines, and the Industrial Revolution was
under way. Lewis Mumford wrote of these times: "The poor
propagated like flies, reached industrial maturity—ten or twelve
years of age—promptly served their term in the new textile mills
or the mines, and died inexpensively." In 1813 an English factory
was destroyed by workers who were angered to the point of revolt
by their misery and that of their youngsters in pitiless factories. The
Industrial Revolution spread to the United States, where the
abundance of iron and coal, its twin underpinnings, coupled with
other natural resources and an inventive people, fanned the flame
of technological change. Railroads spanned the continent and
hastened the development of the west, while in the east the rise of
a steel industry laid the basis for U.S. exploits in building sky-
scrapers, machinery, and bridges. The advent of the motorcar, an
importation from Germany, sparked a wave of development which
has made the name "Detroit" synonymous with auto production.

The nation's great size, its vast reserves of petroleum, and a
restless population spurred the development of the internal combustion engine and its applications. Tractors replaced work horses,
the family automobile became first a luxury, then a necessity, and
now a multiplicity; trucks and buses challenged transportation by
rail, and piston-propelled, later jet-driven, aircraft conquered the
skies. A vast network of concrete and macadam transformed the
nation's surface as the motor industry flooded the highways with
cars, trucks, and buses. Failure to plan for the future cost the nation
dearly as it was forced to undertake metropolitan surgery to allevi-
ate traffic jams on clogged city streets. Fumes from leaded gasoline
and other petroleum products went unnoticed for many years before
smog became a malady of Los Angeles and of an increasing number
of other cities. In the past forty-one years a total of 5.2 billion
pounds of lead compound has been burned in anti-knock gasoline.

Gasoline gave impetus to the Industrial Revolution in America,
but it was electricity and electronics that added a flourish which was

all important. Electrical power modernized United States factories, removing flapping overhead belts and providing controls that were essential to precision machining. Electronics spawned new products like radio and television, now so familiar in every household. Even in pockets of poverty, TV antennas jut up from rickety shacks, and barefoot youths saunter by with portable radios. But the full impact of the new world of technology is yet to be felt; it lies in the field of computers and data-processing machines. The word "automation" has a more emotional connotation, but is less descriptive than the phrase "computer revolution." Automation implies replacement of man by machine; the real meaning of the use of computers is that entirely new classes of machines are now possible. They can do things which man could not do or could do only so slowly as to be worthless.

Consider a few computer applications which have been made in the United States. Airline reservations, involving cross-checks with other airlines and distant cities, are made through the use of computers. Petrochemical plants known as "crackers" are kept in continuous operation and controlled to a fine degree by means of computer systems and sensors. A rocket to the moon is given final guidance based upon computer control. The Western Electric Company manufactures special resistors for satellite application in a computer-ruled production line 110 feet long. No human hand touches the space-age component from start to finish. At Martinsburg, West Virginia, a windowless structure houses banks of computers that process income tax returns, eliminating four thousand persons from such labor. In Madison, Wisconsin, a food processor installed a "wiener tunnel" turning out in about half an hour hot dogs that used to take two hundred women a day and a half to produce.

Modern technology sometimes gives society little warning that it has surprises in store for it. Take, for example, the case of the transistor. This tiny substitute for old-fashioned vacuum tubes was a product of research in the Bell Laboratories. Entirely new techniques had to be worked out to manufacture chemicals to a purity undreamed of in commercial applications. By 1960, some ten years after the transistor was announced, it had created an $8 billion industry.

Other developments, like nuclear power, cast their technological shadows more years in the future, but the impact for society may also be greater. The use of uranium as a cheap substitute for coal in producing electricity was "just around the corner" according to many prophets when the Atomic Energy Commission was created in 1946. Yet nearly two decades later the corner had not been turned although it was then clearly in sight as an economic prospect. In A-power we have a new resource to provide modern technology with vast quantities of electricity—and more to follow when hydrogen power is tamed—thus freeing mankind from dependence upon fossil fuels which cannot last forever. Although it has been a trifle tardy in coming, the new power source is a truly remarkable gift to hand over to future generations. But every gift has its price and uranium poses certain environmental hazards, as we shall see. From the standpoint of the coal miner in West Virginia, uranium is no boon to him, except possibly during the period of the atomic build-up when more coal was needed to provide electricity for atomic production sites. But a million-kilowatt nuclear plant displaces roughly seven thousand workers in the coal business. Fortunately in the nuclear field, the ignition time—namely, the span of years from the conceptual idea to the practical power plant—is about three decades; this should be enough time for society to adjust, providing it is forewarned and tackles the problem.

Technology has scored its most impressive extravaganzas in the military field. Spectaculars in the civilian sector of our economy are less awesome; they lack the imagery and personal impact of the H-bomb and the ICBM. Nonetheless the computer, together with its burgeoning applications, is just as significant to our peacetime economy and it is destined to have the most profound influence on the lives of everyone. Although it is a postwar innovation and has grown to technical adolescence within the past decade, the computer has already invaded many administrative and clerical posts, displacing man. Its amazing power comes from its millionth-of-a-second unit operation which allows it to be programed for the solution of mathematical problems, elaborate bookkeeping and masterminding of completely automated industrial plants. Scientists are now working with nanosecond devices—meaning that the unit time is reduced from one millionth to one billionth of a second. At the same time the wonder world of what the physicists call the "solid state" is yielding microscopic electronic components which make possible smaller and smaller computers. Our experience with modern technology teaches us that the smallest things may give rise to the largest problems.

We live in a time of revolutionary change. The changes, both in their magnitude and in their impact upon society, are new to us. Even as we attempt to react to change, we find acceleration taking place. Through the apparently aimless prying of scientists, power has been unleashed from its ancient bonds and we must now reckon with its proper use and control.

Science and technology offer many choices to our society and to its future. Science itself has no inner wisdom or aim which makes the choices obvious. Nor are the scientists anointed with special authority to decide which choices to make. The choices should be made freely with the full counsel of scientists, but they should be made by the people as a whole.

René Dubos in *The Dreams of Reason* analyzes the interaction of the scientist and society and in effect writes the following prescription:

It is for society, of course, to decide what goals it wishes to reach and what risks it is willing to take. But it is the task of the scientific community to formulate as clearly as possible and to make public the probable consequences of any step that it takes and of any action that it advocates. In other words, the responsibility of the scientist does not stop when he has developed the knowledge and techniques that lead to a process or a product. Beyond that, he must secure and make public the kind of information on which the social body as a whole can base the value judgments that alone will decide long range policies.

This prescription is rather hard for the individual scientist to swallow. He is apt to be a specialist absorbed in his own researches and quite ignorant or poorly informed of things outside his niche. We have seen that the "scientific community" is mythical; it is a convenient term to apply rhetorically but it no longer rings a bell practically. So far as federal science policy is concerned, there is an elite which determines how funds shall be allocated and this is the essence of science policy. Dr. Donald N. Michael has observed: "Policy now springs from resolving disputes for priority among various projects. It is made in many places, from the Pentagon to the Department of Agriculture, as well as in those offices assigned part of the policy-making task. But nowhere do the social implications of science have a basic part in the formulation of policy."

Michael's conclusion, applied here to science as opposed to technology, raises questions of particular significance to the White House advisers. How do they make the "value judgments" and communicate with the public as René Dubos recommends? Is a scientist competent to make such decisions, and if so, by what right or by what training?

George Bernard Shaw said: "Science is always wrong. It never solves a problem without creating ten more." President Kennedy phrased it from a neutral angle: "I recognize with each door that we unlock we see perhaps ten doors that we never knew existed." But science is neither right nor wrong; it is an unbiased discipline to be used as man wills.

In the past the choices which man made among the alternatives proffered by science and technology were not catastrophic in their consequences, at least not always to those who chose. The Chinese invented gunpowder but it was Europe that nearly chose to blow itself asunder in a series of deliberate actions. Today the time span between concept and catastrophe may be small; this is the ugly portent of modern technology. And the destructive potential of nuclear energy mounted so high in the early sixties that by mid-decade the United States found itself at an historic turning point.

America's nuclear arsenal swelled to such incredible proportions that further additions became quite unnecessary. The vast empire of military research and development facilities, which at one time gulped down almost $8 billion in one year, could be reoriented toward other national needs. The same forces which can annihilate may also be used to create. If science is to play a key role in the Great Society, as President Johnson envisions, then here is the opportunity to give it new direction in the service of society. Of course, it is still possible that the world might plunge ahead in a mad arms race and the United States be converted to a weapons culture. But the year 1964 seemed to mark a point of historical pause—a time when the Soviet Union was amenable to a letup in the Cold War and a time when Red China could not yet threaten our national security. It was a propitious time to lay the foundations for a Great Society.

Tom Wicker, the New York *Times* correspondent, proposed the following definition of this society: "A promised land in which there will be no poverty, no illiteracy, no unemployment, no prejudice, no slums, no polluted streams, no delinquency, and few Republicans." Leaving out the terminal quip, these are all noble objectives of a democratic society. Unfortunately, the nature of the political dialogue in the 1964 Presidential campaign did not illuminate the character of the Great Society. President Johnson did not at, least in 1964, define the role that science might play in the building of a Great Society.

President Kennedy had related science to the needs of society in a speech to the National Academy of Sciences, concentrating on four points:

1. Conservation and development of natural resources.
2. Understanding and use of the resources of the sea.
3. The study of the atmosphere.
4. The control of the effects of our own scientific experiments.

The Kennedy program for study and use of the planet's three environments, air, sea, and land, acknowledged that "as science investigates the natural environment, it also modifies it, and that modification may have incalculable consequences for evil as well as for good." More specifically, Kennedy stated that "science has the power for the first time in history now to undertake experiments with premeditation which can irreversibly alter our biological and physical environment on a global scale."

If one distinguishes between science and technology—not generally done in public pronouncements—then President Kennedy's admonition points to technology as a potential tyrant for society. Technological change offers great prospects for improving man's environment, but he who seeks the rewards must be wary of a Pandoralike surprise. This is especially true when we consider that *Homo technicus* will be seeking to remodel nature on a grand scale. In fact, if technology is to be exploited for its peacetime benefits, then large-scale alternatives must be provided to take up the slack left by diminishing efforts in the area of military technology. National technological goals need to be established to give adequate outlet to intellectual daring and to consume human energy for useful purposes. Kennedy's decision to reach for the moon was made in this vein, but it was a jagged venture which Polykarp Kusch, Nobel prize-winning physicist, criticized:

As a citizen—perhaps I should say as a moral man—I have been very gravely concerned about the relationship of the space program to other national goals and purposes. I think we have great national needs which far outweigh the need for the exploration of space.

I think that any major national effort should be evaluated in terms of its effects on the lives of people, on their standard of living, their health and the opportunities they may find for leading satisfactory lives. By "people" I mean the totality of all Americans, and I mean their progeny for many generations.

Kusch's critique of the U.S. space effort brings down to earth the criteria for assessing national priorities in technological ventures. It also stresses the long-term values that must be considered, and raises the issue of national planning in relation to technology. Planning on a scale commensurate with technological opportunity and long-term human needs is essentially new to America.

People living in the year 2000 may look back and wonder why America never made any coherent National Systems Analysis—of the type that will surely be standard then. They may be puzzled by the fact that numerous partial analyses were made of specific needs for a decade or two but that no over-all plan emerged for long-term solutions, though if our post-observers one-third century from now are compassionate, they will recognize the dilemma of gearing large-scale technological planning to the demands of economics and politics.

But anticipation of future requirements is not beyond human capability. It required no genius, for example, to look at the mass production of automobiles in the twenties and to foresee that American cities were not designed to accommodate the torrent of transportation which would spew through city streets by midcentury. The thirties presented a time of opportunity for massive metropolitan surgery to open up new arteries of access for vehicles. Property values were low; men and material were available for public works. Suddenly in the early forties the nation awoke from its economic stupor and under the artificial stimulus of war it spent in one year more than had been expended during a full decade. Then for ten years after the war the nation's cities expanded, grew more congested; property values spiraled and wages soared; finally in the fifties the federal government financed a highway program. By then it was very late to keep up with the hemorrhage of cars. Detroit speed-cultists crammed more horsepower under the hood and tantalized every motorist with a speedometer reading up to 120 mph. Yet the average speed through city traffic read 20 mph and all too frequently the speedometer needle remained stuck at zero.

Just as the modern car beguiles the driver with a promise of 120-mph speed, both illegal and impractical except on Great Salt flats, jet planes tempt designers to Mach 3 and higher velocities. But man and nature impose certain restrictions of a rather fundamental character. Sonic boom, a nasty concomitant of supersonic travel, appears to suggest no easy solution. Time is another unalterable factor which plagues air commerce; for example, economy demands maximum in-air employment of expensive aircraft but this plays havoc with the air traveler's arrival and departure times, so that many a passenger would choose slower flight at more convenient hours. Reducing transatlantic travel times from 6 to 2.5 hours would probably not satisfy any urgent need. To cut costs would be far more useful but there seems little prospect for cut-rate supersonic flight. Technology has advanced to a point where intercontinental distances are comfortably spanned; the dimensions of "the great globe itself" are no longer large. To assert this is not to embrace complacency: it is to recognize that there are certain practical limits to mass transportation. To be sure, rockets go faster than airplanes, but this does not constitute a persuasive argument for transporting people ballistically.

Recognition that there are practical or economic limits imposed upon the performance of technology is, in fact, one of the basic reasons for adopting a national-planning approach to satisfying future requirements for natural resources. In many respects the national long-term needs are too immense to be met by short-term limited measures. For example, an adequate supply of good water will be needed for the future, yet desalination techniques appear to hold only limited promise for certain areas, and a program of continental engineering proportions may be required to assure a full measure of pure water for the North American continent. Already southwestern states quarrel over water from the Colorado River, and Mexico mourns the saline water it receives from the United States. It would seem to make sense to establish a Continental Water Authority (TVA on a monumental scale) in which the run-off of precipitation is redirected by a system of engineered watersheds and waterways. The earthworks for such a program of land-sculpturing would make any similar efforts of the past look trivial. Such a program, if started by 1970, could stretch out to A.D. 2000 and involve a total of $100 billion. It could be tied with a system of National Weather Control when atmospheric engineering becomes feasible.

Since research and technology presently claim such a considerable portion of federal outlays, they cannot be extrapolated for fifteen years into the future without specifying the anticipated Gross

National Product (GNP). The author makes the following projection to the year 1980. The 1980 GNP is assumed to be $1.3 trillion, not an audacious estimate by any means and one that may turn out to be too low. If the leveling off of R & D expenditures at $16 billion per annum for a $600 billion GNP is interpreted as a ratio which Congress and society will accept in the future, then we can make a Simple Simon projection of $35 billion for research and development in 1980. It would be surprising if the figure were less than this; a lower figure would reflect popular resentment of science and technology and a dissatisfaction with its accomplishments. The public might, for example, react from a momentary thrill on Apollo Day, when men land on the moon for the first time, to disillusion, when nothing is translated into a payoff for the average citizen. On the other hand, if R & D is successful in the biomedical field during the seventies, the public might back rising budgets for science. Much will depend upon the performance of science and technology during the seventies and upon the national wisdom shown in selecting technological goals.

Given a $35-billion-per-year R & D budget for 1980, the biggest unknown in slicing this fat pie is the slice for defense. Defense R & D funds have been pared back in the mid-sixties, and prediction of such expenditures in the seventies is hazardous because no one can foresee the state of the world then. If a semipeaceful condition obtains, then a modest R & D budget would suffice to take care of the nation's military technology. It would be fatuous to assume such a peaceful world that military R & D would be abandoned. Indeed, there would be a real need for arms-control technology to ensure that agreements on arms were kept. The author makes the assumption that by 1980 the nation will spend $10 billion per year on R & D for arms and arms control, leaving $25 billion to be divided up into nondefense efforts. First, I would assume $7 billion for basic research, and half of this sum a direct grant to educational institutions as lump-sum commitments. Then I would divide up the remaining $18 billion for the following technological programs:

1. Bioengineering Programs	$4 billion
2. Continental Engineering and Land Resource Conservation	4
3. Ocean Engineering	3
4. Space Programs	3
5. Atmospheric Programs	2
6. National Data System	1
7. All other	1

Item 1. This allocation of $4 billion would represent biomedical applications resulting from intensive research during the seventies. It would, for example, reflect systems approaches to the problem of supplying replacement parts of worn out or defective human organs. Emphasis would also be placed upon instrumental techniques for early detection of oncoming disease through automatic analysis of body effluents.

Item 2. The line between R & D activities and public works would probably be blurred during the next decades and it might be better to speak of R D & E activities. Continental engineering for water conservation and controlled run-off has been mentioned. Regulation of the Great Lakes water system would be an integral part of such a program. So, too, would be development of methods for dealing with water pollution. Resource conservation would include thorough inventory of the nation's mineral and fuel resources and development of a long-range program for ensuring their adequate supply.

Item 3. Oceanic resources, especially mineral, are just beginning to be appreciated. Techniques are now being evolved which make it feasible to tap ocean-floor resources. The continental shelves lend themselves to exploitation but special *in situ* processing may make deep-ocean mining practicable. Certain oceanic areas also make attractive colossal engineering projects for diverting ocean currents and altering local climates.

Item 4. Once men land on the moon in the early seventies, the United States will presumably confine its interplanetary flights to instrumented missions. Manned missions to Mars are not possible in the seventies, and a major national decision will be necessary if such missions are to be accomplished in the eighties. The assumption is that space exploration will involve reduced expenditures. However, close to earth it would be expected that extensive applications would be found for communications satellites.

Item 5. The atmosphere is the most volatile and unpredictable of the three environments which comprise man's home. R & D activities focused on understanding the nature of weather and climate should allow more accurate predictions of weather. Weather control should become possible on a limited scale in the seventies, and the modification of climate appears to be a possibility in the following decade.

Item 6. The rapid production of scientific data and the proliferation of specialized publications is sufficient justification for a National Data Center. This would take the form of a centralized data storage and retrieval center connected to ancillary subcenters in cities and towns. Scientists would not be forced to thumb through magazines or reports but would gain access to the pertinent literature through a computer search and a readout of data from the National Data Center.

Item 7. This miscellany would include agricultural research of an applied nature, and development of such communication, transportation, and other devices not provided for through industrial programs.

The $25 billion R & D budget is more than triple the present nondefense budget over a period of fifteen years. The goals encompassed are obvious ones which represent a continuation of man's conquest of his environment, but it will probably be harder to persuade Congress to authorize continental engineering than to fund a lunar program. That which is closer to home and more familiar is apt to undergo tougher congressional scrutiny. The establishment of national goals in technology coincides with a time of cultural crisis, when society is in transition, battered by science and its technological offspring with a series of awesome shocks. An America long used to isolation from direct military assault finds itself vulnerable to attack and forced to put its faith in a system of weapon deterrents of unknown effectiveness. This alone is enough to shake any society to its core. But at the same time the output of highly organized science presses down upon the average man and makes him feel small and intimidated. How can he as the smallest democratic denominator play a role in setting goals for something he does not understand? He is aware in an imperfect way that modern science has made giant strides in the advance of knowledge—that the stars and atoms, the largest and the smallest of material things, have surrendered many of their long-kept secrets. He may even be aware that breakthroughs have been scored in discerning the inner architecture of the living cell. Life, alas, is no longer simple, and society must adjust to the driving impetus of forces it does not fully comprehend. In a sense our society is no longer open in the way Lewis Mumford described the Greek city-state: "All that men did was open to inspection alike in the market, or worship, the law court, the council, the gymnasium."

Charles Frankel has written: "The advent of science, together with the increase of technical, specialized knowledge in every domain, has fundamentally altered the condition under which the ideal of an open society has to be pursued." The inability of the citizen to understand science and technology effectively closes off part of society and severely hinders the formulation of technological goals. It is here that the scientist as citizen bears a special responsibility for restoring dialogue within a democracy. Unless he makes the effort to translate and interpret scientific and technical issues, the bulk of his countrymen may be condemned to intellectual serfdom and blind acquiescence. At best democracy functions on a highly intricate basis of subtle information flow and feedback. Those in high office may even persuade themselves that it is futile to attempt to carry on a dialogue on issues such as ballistic missile defense or some project equally ensnarled in technology. Society may become a captive of a technological elite. President Eisenhower did warn of such a scientific-technological elite and he gave the antidote: "It is the task of statesmanship to mold, to balance, and to integrate these and other forces, new and old, within the principles of our democratic system—ever aiming toward the supreme goals of our free society." The antidote however could be sugar water or a potent draught for democracy, depending upon *who* molded, balanced, and integrated the forces and *how* they operated. Always there would remain the fundamental problem of converting the goals, chosen by a few, into the objectives of the many.

If technology is so enticing that society is powerless to resist its charms, then it can become the Great Dictator of our times. There is a real danger that science and its rampageous offspring—technology—may become a modern Moloch if not brought under control. The very word "control" strikes fear into the heart of a true scientist, who fears any restraint upon his endeavors. But the control involved here is essentially one of policy determination and public safeguards to lessen or ward off the hazards of hostile technology. Control is necessary not only to protect society against the ravages of deleterious forces, but also to achieve the full benefits of science. Such control must of course be wisely exercised and this in turn means that policy must be made by those who are literate in science.

Just how far the dialogue can be extended to the populace is a moot point. The present educational attainments of the electorate make it difficult to establish good communication in scientific and technical fields. In the future, as the educational level is raised, the dialogue may be easier, but for the present it will probably have to be restricted to those who can understand the new jargon of scientists and technologists and to those who catch the sense of the conversation even though they are not literate in technical matters. After all, on the issue of water conservation one does not have to be an expert hydrologist to appreciate that the nation badly needs more water. Here the common sense of the average citizen still stands him in good stead. But when he is confronted with value judgments involving a choice of technological undertakings or a determination of the scale of competing projects, his common sense may no longer be so valuable. Yet choices will have to be made— some on a monumental scale.

If society abdicates to the scientists, or if there is no effective dialogue, then the focus of decision will be upon the scientists. Their value judgments will be imposed on society. Like any other

group in our society, science has its full share of personalities—
wide-gauge and narrow-track minds, sages and scoundrels, trail-
blazers and path-followers, altruists and connivers. The goals of
science are noble but not always ennobling. Its practitioners may
be deeply touched or little moved by their researches, insofar as
they relate them to society. A researcher's discoveries may win him
a Nobel Prize but he may have little sense of the impact of his
work upon society. Scientists as a group probably have no better
sense of human values than any other group; some observers even
believe that, because too often the specialists tend to shut themselves off from the rest of society, theirs may be too parochial a set
of values. To say that science seeks the truth does not endow
scientists as a group with special wisdom of what is good for society. Furthermore, scientists have no single community within
which there is a common set of values. The sociology of science
is in a primitive state and is little studied. Yet the apartness of
science, its strange dimension, and its powerful manifestations in
applications combine to throw an unnatural light around this new
subculture. The specialists of science take on the appearance of a
new priesthood, and the "miracles" of science, for that is what they
must seem to be to the uninformed, can become the basis of cult-
worship, even of a new religion.

The British scientist-philosopher Jacob Bronowski has recently
expressed a fear of the expert: "A world run by specialists for the
ignorant is, and will be, a slave world." In the nature of things, the
specialist of today represents a high degree of technical training. A
rather high level of intelligence is necessary for the novitiates to
gain entry into the Ph.D. ranks. Thus if the scientists become the
dominant decision-makers or even advisers, a separative society is
a real danger. The nation's first President competent in science,
Thomas Jefferson, wrote:

To furnish the citizens with full and correct information is a matter
of the highest importance. If we think them not enlightened enough to
exercise their control with a wholesome discretion, the remedy is not to
take it from them but to inform their discretion by education.

Jefferson's advice is difficult to apply today. The educational breach is formidable and the corrective therapy takes time. Unfortunately, the technological tyrant in our midst is impatient and will not sit out a decade or two while the nation educates itself to the technology of today. Perhaps it might be better to suggest that the newly emerging generation of scientists be required to serve a kind of postgraduate internship on the relation of science to society. At the very least the formal education of scientists should make sure that they emerge from universities with the philosophy of an architect rather than that of a technical apprentice.

Modern man has come too quickly to the bounty of elemental power known only to the stars. This knowledge has triggered a tumultuous technology which threatens to diminish man while at the same time it proffers the keys to a Utopia beyond the dreams of a Thomas More. Society cannot expect that the scientists who fashioned the early experiments and brought forth the Jinni hold the power of putting them back in the bottle. For better or for worse the forces have been unleashed and society must reckon with them. To design and apply the proper controls is most certainly a supreme test of our society.

John Kennedy was the first President of the United States to view fully the impact of science upon society. One month before his life ended, he addressed himself to the subject and gave these thoughts to a national scientific conference:

We are bound to grope for a time as we grapple with problems without precedent in human history, but wisdom is the child of experience. In the years since man unlocked the power stored within the atom, the world has made progress, halting but effective, towards bringing that power under human control. The challenge, in short, may be our salvation. As we begin to master the potentialities of modern science we move toward a new era in which science can fulfill its creative promise and help bring into existence the happiest society the world has ever known.

INDEX

Soviet Union (*Continued*)
  meaning of 100-megaton bomb,
    144–145
  military strength, 141–142
  nuclear might, 109
  nuclear tests, 145
  opposition to foreign inspectors, 119
  proposal to cease nuclear testing,
    1958, 135
  retaliatory capability, 142–143
  U-2 incident, 141, 145
Space program, 19, 27, 154, 162–174,
  178–179, 191–192, 195, 220
  economic consequences of altering,
    178–179
  emphasis on military implications of
    space, 164
Space science, 197
Space Sciences Board, National Academy of Sciences, 168, 169–170,
  172, 173
Space testing, 136
"Space trucks," 169, 171
Special Assistant to the President for
  Science and Technology, 194
Sputnik I, 19, 135, 163, 190, 193
Sputnik II, 194
Stagg Field, University of Chicago, 41
Stanford University, 17, 21
Stans, Maurice H., 164
State Department, U.S., 135, 139, 148,
  210
*State of Science and Its Prospects for
  Society, The,* 198
Stearns, Joyce, 76
Steel industry, 214
Steelman, John R., 193
Stevenson, Adlai, 121, 129, 130, 135,
  181
Stimson, Henry, 70, 73, 74–75, 76, 77,
  81–82, 83, 87–88
Stocks, glamour, 33–34
Strategic Air Command, 109–110, 111
Strauss, Lewis L., 103, 109, 125–126,
  134–135, 143, 185
Strontium-90, 66, 127–129
Submarines, 142, 145
Sufficiency, nuclear, 146, 149
Summerfield, Martin, 25
"Sunshine unit," 129
Superbombs, 143–145
System Development Corp., 35

Szilard, Leo, 45–50, 52, 53, 54, 55, 57,
  59, 61, 63, 69, 70–72, 73, 74,
  76, 79–80, 83, 88, 89, 92, 93,
  111, 114, 115, 132–133, 187–
  189
  and the Einstein letter, 45–50, 63
  petition for international control of
    the atomic bomb, 79–80, 83
  "political invention," 187–189

Tactical atomic bombs, 105
Tall, John S., 183
Tantalus, 1
Taylor, Glen, 94
Taylor, Lauriston, 31
Technology, 24, 27, 30, 37, 63, 64,
  66, 139, 147, 211–229
  accelerating trend of, 213
  criteria for assessing national priorities in, 220
  danger of by-products of, 66
  distinguished from science, 220
  impact upon society, 213–229
  instrumentation, 27, 64, 139
  limits imposed upon, 222
  mass organization of, 63
  in the military field, 216
  need for anticipation of future requirements, 221
  need for national planning approach,
    221–222
  research and development costs, 212
  time span between concept and
    catastrophe, 218
Television, 215
Teller, Edward, 46, 49–50, 52, 106,
  107, 108, 134, 138, 140, 185
Tennessee Valley Authority (TVA),
  102, 103
Test ban proposals, 129–130, 135
Tests, nuclear:
  "big-hole" theory of nuclear test
    cheating, 140, 141
  Bikini Atoll tests, 120, 121–122,
    123, 125
  Blanca test, 138
  curtailment of, 123
  England, 146
  fallout. *See* Fallout
  France, 146
  Hardtack series, 137–138, 139
  H-bomb, 120–123

RALPH E. LAPP is a distinguished scientist, author, and lecturer whose books include *The Voyage of the Lucky Dragon, Roads to Discovery,* and *Man and Space: The Next Decade.*

He received his Ph.D. at the University of Chicago in 1945. His research in cosmic rays was followed by research on nuclear energy for the Manhattan Project; at the end of World War II, he was appointed assistant director of the Argonne National Laboratory, consulting scientist for the Bikini Bomb Tests, and served as science adviser on the War Department general staff from 1946–1947. He then became the head of the nuclear physics branch of the Office of Naval Research and since 1950 has served as a consulting physicist for the Nuclear Science Service. Recently, he became a founder of Quadri-Science, Inc., in Washington, D.C.

His articles and lectures on radioactive fallout and radiation hazards have had national and international influence. He has pioneered in arousing the public and government to the impact of science upon society. Dr. Lapp lives in Alexandria, Virginia.